西游记

[明] 吴承恩 原著

李梓萌 马娴 改编

Journey to the West
(Abridged)

Sinolingua
华语教学出版社

First Edition   2017
Second Printing   2019

ISBN 978-7-5138-1329-7
Copyright 2017 by Sinolingua Co., Ltd
Published by Sinolingua Co., Ltd
24 Baiwanzhuang Street, Beijing 100037, China
Tel: (86) 10-68320585   68997826
Fax: (86) 10-68997826   68326333
http://www.sinolingua.com.cn
E-mail: hyjx@sinolingua.com.cn
Facebook: www.facebook.com/sinolingua
Printed by Beijing Jinghua Hucais Printing Co., Ltd

Printed in the People's Republic of China

编者的话

对于广大汉语学习者来说，要想快速提高汉语水平，扩大阅读量是很有必要的。"彩虹桥"汉语分级读物为汉语学习者提供了一系列有趣、有用的汉语阅读材料。本系列读物按照词汇量进行分级，力求用限定的词汇讲述精彩的故事。本套读物主要有以下特点：

一、分级精准，循序渐进。我们参考"新汉语水平考试（HSK）词汇表"（2012 年修订版）、《汉语国际教育用音节汉字词汇等级划分（国家标准）》和《常用汉语 1500 高频词语表》等词汇分级标准，结合《欧洲语言教学与评估框架性共同标准》（CEFR），设计了一套适合汉语学习者的"彩虹桥"词汇分级标准。本系列读物分为 7 个级别（入门级*、1 级、2 级、3 级、4 级、5 级、6 级），供不同水平的汉语学习者选择，每个级别故事的生词数量不超过本级别对应词汇量的 20%。随着级别的升高，故事的篇幅逐渐加长。本系列读物与 HSK、CEFR 的对应级别，各级词汇量以及每本书的字数详见下表。

---

* 入门级（Starter）在封底用 S 标识。

级别	入门级	1级	2级	3级	4级	5级	6级
对应级别	HSK1 CEFR A1	HSK1-2 CEFR A1-A2	HSK2-3 CEFR A2-B1	HSK3 CEFR A2-B1	HSK3-4 CEFR B1	HSK4 CEFR B1-B2	HSK5 CEFR B2-C1
词汇量	150	300	500	750	1 000	1 500	2 500
字数	1 000	2 500	5 000	7 500	10 000	15 000	25 000

二、**故事精彩，题材多样**。本套读物选材的标准就是"精彩"，所选的故事要么曲折离奇，要么感人至深，对读者构成奇妙的吸引力。选题广泛取材于中国的神话传说、民间故事、文学名著、名人传记和历史故事等，让汉语学习者在阅读中潜移默化地了解中国的文化和历史。

三、**结构合理，实用性强**。"彩虹桥"系列读物的每一本书中，除了中文故事正文之外，都配有主要人物的中英文介绍、生词英文注释及例句、故事正文的英文翻译、练习题和生词表，方便读者阅读和理解故事内容，提升汉语阅读能力。练习题主要采用客观题，题型多样，难度适中，并附有参考答案，既可供汉语教师在课堂上教学使用，又可供汉语学习者进行自我水平检测。

如果您对本系列读物有什么想法，比如推荐精彩故事、提出改进意见等，请发邮件到 liuxiaolin@sinolingua. com.cn，与我们交流探讨。也可以关注我们的微信公众号 CHQRainbowBridge，随时与我们交流互动。同时，微信公众号会不定期发布有关"彩虹桥"的出版信息，以及汉语阅读、中国文化小知识等。

韩　颖　刘小琳

Preface

For students who study Chinese as a foreign language, it's crucial for them to enlarge the scope of their reading to improve their comprehension skills. The "Rainbow Bridge" Graded Chinese Reader series is designed to provide a collection of interesting and useful Chinese reading materials. This series grades each volume by its vocabulary level and brings the learners into every scene through vivid storytelling. The series has the following features:

I. A gradual approach by grading the volumes based on vocabulary levels. We have consulted the New HSK Vocabulary (2012 Revised Edition), the *Graded Chinese Syllables, Characters and Words for the Application of Teaching Chinese to the Speakers of Other Languages (National Standard)* and the 1,500 Commonly Used High Frequency Chinese Vocabulary, along with the Common European Framework of Reference for Languages (CEFR) to design the "Rainbow Bridge" vocabulary grading standard. The series is divided into seven levels (Starter*, Level 1, Level 2, Level 3, Level 4, Level 5 and Level 6) for students at different stages in their Chinese education to choose from. For each level, new words are no more than 20% of the vocabulary amount as specified in the corresponding HSK and CEFR levels. As the levels progress, the passage length will in turn increase. The following table indicates the corresponding "Rainbow Bridge" level, HSK and CEFR levels, the vocabulary amount, and number of characters.

---

*   Represented by "S" on the back cover.

Level	Starter	1	2	3	4	5	6
HSK/ CEFR Level	HSK1 CEFR A1	HSK1-2 CEFR A1-A2	HSK2-3 CEFR A2-B1	HSK3 CEFR A2-B1	HSK3-4 CEFR B1	HSK4 CEFR B1-B2	HSK5 CEFR B2-C1
Vocabulary	150	300	500	750	1,000	1,500	2,500
Characters	1,000	2,500	5,000	7,500	10,000	15,000	25,000

II. Intriguing stories on various themes. The series features engaging stories known for their twists and turns as well as deeply touching plots. The readers will find it a joyful experience to read the stories. The topics are selected from Chinese mythology, legends, folklore, literary classics, biographies of renowned people and historical tales. Such wide-ranging topics exert an invisible, yet formative, influence on readers' understanding of Chinese culture and history.

III. Reasonably structured and easy to use. For each volume of the "Rainbow Bridge" series, apart from a Chinese story, we also provide an introduction to the main characters in Chinese and English, new words with English explanations and sample sentences, and an English translation of the story, followed by comprehension exercises and a vocabulary list to help users read and understand the story and improve their Chinese reading skills. The exercises are mainly presented as objective questions that take on various forms with moderate difficulty. Moreover, keys to the exercises are also provided. The series can be used by teachers in class or by students for self-study.

If you have any questions, comments or suggestions about the series, please email us at liuxiaolin@sinolingua.com.cn. You can also exchange ideas with us via our WeChat account: CHQRainbowBridge. This account will provide updates on the series along with Chinese reading materials and cultural tips.

Han Ying and Liu Xiaolin

目　　录
Contents

1. 美猴王出生

主要人物和地点：
Main Characters and Places

美猴王（Měihóuwáng）：从仙石中孕育而生的石猴。他聪明、调皮、嫉恶如仇，叛逆却又忠诚。后取名孙悟空，跟随菩提祖师练就了一身本领，武艺高强，勇敢过人，所使用的兵器是如意金箍棒。后来拜唐僧为师，一路上降妖伏魔，历经八十一难，最后取回佛经修成正果。

Handsome Monkey King: A monkey bred from a fairy stone. He is brilliant, but mischievous; he hates evil and is rebellious but loyal. He is later named Sun Wukong and gains profound abilities in all aspects by learning from Subhuti. He not only excels in martial arts, but is also extremely brave. The Gold-banded Cudgel is his weapon. Later, he apprentices for Monk Xuanzang and helps him subdue demons and monsters during their journey. After overcoming 81 tribulations, he finally obtains the authentic Buddhist scriptures and attains Buddhahood.

花果山（Huāguǒ Shān）：位于东胜神洲傲来国，此山吸取了日月精华，是孙悟空的出生地。

Mount Huaguo (Flowers and Fruit Mountain): Empowered by the sun and the moon, it is situated in the country of Aolai in the Eastern Continent of Superior Deity.

水帘洞（Shuǐlián Dòng）：美猴王和其他的猴子们住的地方，由于这个洞的外面有一条大瀑布，就像水做的帘子一样，所以叫作水帘洞。

Shuilian Cave (Water Curtain Cave): It is the place where Monkey King and other monkeys live. It is so named because there is a waterfall that flows over the entrance of the cave, acting as a curtain, which is called 水帘 (water curtain) in Chinese.

很久以前，海① 里有一座山②，叫<u>花果山</u>。山上有一块巨大的石头。突然有一天③，石头裂④ 开了，里面⑤跳⑥ 出来了一只石猴⑦。他刚出生，就会跑⑧ 会跳，眼睛里还有金⑨ 光。它跟其他的猴子在一起生活，日子过得很开心。

有一天，天气特别热，猴子们⑩ 都跑到一条小河⑪里玩。它们在河里走了很远，想看看河水是从哪儿来的。它们走到河水的尽头⑫，看到有瀑布⑬ 从山上流⑭ 下来，瀑布后面有一个山洞⑮。

猴子们很好奇，特别想知道山洞里是什么，可是水很大，它们都有点儿⑯ 害怕。

这时候，一只老猴子站

① 海 (hǎi) n. ocean, sea
e.g., 看，海里有鱼。
② 山 (shān) n. mountain, hill
e.g., 明天我要去爬山。
③ 天 (tiān) n. day
e.g., 你哪天有空？
④ 裂 (liè) v. crack, break open, split
e.g., 杯子裂了。
⑤ 里面 (lǐmiàn) n. inside
e.g., 里面太黑，什么都看不见。
⑥ 跳 (tiào) v. jump, leap
e.g., 你赶快跳过去吧。
⑦ 石猴 (shíhóu) n. stone monkey
e.g.,《西游记》里的主角是只石猴。
⑧ 跑 (pǎo) v. run
e.g., 她比我跑得快。
⑨ 金 (jīn) adj. golden
e.g., 那件衣服是金色的。
⑩ 们 (men) suf. (added after a personal pronoun or a noun to show plural number)
⑪ 小河 (xiǎo hé) n. stream, small river
e.g., 小河里有鱼。
⑫ 尽头 (jìntóu) n. end
e.g., 似乎永远也看不到海的尽头。
⑬ 瀑布 (pùbù) n. waterfall
e.g., 这条瀑布真大。
⑭ 流 (liú) v. flow
e.g., 河水向东流。
⑮ 山洞 (shāndòng) n. cave
e.g., 山洞里面太黑了，什么也看不见。
⑯ 有点儿 (yǒudiǎnr) adv. a little, a bit
e.g., 别走了，我有点儿累。

① 猴王 (hóuwáng) *n.*
monkey king
e.g., 所有的猴子都害
怕猴王。

② 床 (chuáng) *n* bed
床下面好像有什么东西。

③ 刮 (guā) *v.* (wind)
blow
e.g., 外面刮大风了。

④ 风 (fēng) *n.* wind
e.g., 风太大了，咱们
一会再出去。

出来对大家说："谁要是敢走进山洞里看看，谁就当我们的猴王①！"

石猴听了马上就说："我进去看看！"

它跳过瀑布，走进山洞。这个山洞就像一个大房间，里面的东西都是石头做的，有石椅、石床②、石盆、石碗等。房间里还有一个大石头，上面刻着"水帘洞"。原来这个山洞就叫"水帘洞"。

过了一会儿，石猴又从瀑布里跳出来了。它对大家说："里面真是一个好地方，什么都有。如果住在里面，无论外面刮③风④还是下雨，我们都不用害怕了。"

猴子们听了，都跳进

① 神奇 (shénqí) *adj.*
magical
e.g., 这个发明太神奇了!

了瀑布里，去看那个神奇①的山洞。里面果然跟石猴说的一样可爱。它们看看这里、摸摸那里，高兴得又叫又跳。

从此，水帘洞就成了猴子们的家。石猴也当上了猴王，它给自己取了一个新名字——"美猴王"。

思考题：
Answer the following questions according to the story.

1. 石猴是从哪里来的?
2. 为什么猴子们让石猴当了大王?
3. 石猴给自己取的新名字叫什么?

2. 学习本领

主要人物和地点：
Main Characters and Places

菩提祖师（Pútí Zǔshī）：既通道教也通佛教的大仙，法力高深，弟子众多，教化广泛，深得当地百姓尊敬。他教会了孙悟空七十二变和筋斗云，是孙悟空的第一个师傅。

Subhuti: A great immortal who is knowledgeable in both Taoism and Buddhism. Because of his great power, he has a large number of disciples and is widely respected by locals. He teaches Monkey King the 72 Methods of Transformation and Somersault Cloud, and is Monkey King's first master.

孙悟空（Sūn Wùkōng）：菩提祖师给美猴王取的新名字。

Sun Wukong: The name bestowed by Subhuti on Monkey King, which literally means awakened to emptiness.

三星洞（Sānxīng Dòng）：神仙菩提祖师住的地方。

Sanxing Cave: The home of Subhuti, which literally means three stars cave.

① 活 (huó) *v.* live (up)
e.g., 这只小鸟还活着。

② 师父 (shīfu) *n.* master, an honorific title especially used by apprentices or disciples to address those who teach them craftsmanship
e.g., 我跟师父学了很多本领。

③ 长生不老 (chángshēng-bùlǎo) *v.* live forever and never grow old, be immortal
e.g., 没有人能长生不老。

④ 第 (dì) *aux.* (used before a numeral to form an ordinal number)
e.g., 这次考试我得了第一名。

⑤ 后 (hòu) *n.* afterwards
e.g., 三天后你再来找我。

⑥ 神仙 (shénxiān) *n.* an immortal who has supernatural power
e.g., 传说中，神仙可以长生不老。

五百年过去了。一天，美猴王对大家说："我们现在很开心，可是有一天还是得死。"于是，大家都伤心起来。

一只老猴子说："如果想永远活①下去，只有去找个厉害的师父②，学习长生不老③的本领。"美猴王听了，第④二天就出发去找师父了。

几天后⑤，美猴王来到了"三星洞"。这里住着一个神仙⑥，叫菩提祖师。菩提祖师答应做美猴王的师父，还给他取了一个新名字，叫孙悟空。

七年过去了。一天，师父问孙悟空："你想学什么？"

孙悟空回答："师父教

什么，我就学什么。"

师父说："占卜①？"

孙悟空问："能长生不老吗？"

师父说："不能。"

孙悟空说："不学。"

师父又说："炼丹②呢？"

孙悟空问："能长生不老吗？"

师父回答："不能。"

孙悟空摇摇头③："不学，不学。"

师父生气地说："你这也不学，那也不学，到底想干什么？"然后用戒尺④在孙悟空的头上敲了三下，就走了。

大家都埋怨⑤这只不懂事⑥的猴子。可是孙悟空不但不生气，反而很高兴。半

① 占卜 (zhānbǔ) v.
practice divination
e.g., 我想学占卜。

② 炼丹 (liàndān) v.
make pills (as a Taoist
practice)
e.g., 道士会炼丹。

③ 头 (tóu) n. head
e.g., 你头上是什么
东西？

④ 戒尺 (jièchǐ) n.
(in ancient China)
teacher's paddle
used for punishing
pupils
e.g., 以前老师用戒
尺打学生。

⑤ 埋怨 (mányuàn) v.
blame, complain
e.g., 别再埋怨他了。

⑥ 懂事 (dǒngshì) v.
be sensible or con-
siderate
e.g., 她是个懂事的女
孩。

夜，当大钟①敲了三下的时候，孙悟空来到了师父的房间。原来师父用戒尺打孙悟空三下，是想告诉他三更②再来偷偷学习。

孙悟空不但跟师父学会了长生不老的本领，还学习了七十二变¹和翻筋斗云²。孙悟空变得越来越得意，还经常在大家面前③炫耀④。

一天，师父对孙悟空说："你的性格太张扬⑤，又喜欢炫耀，迟早要给我惹祸⑥，你还是走吧。"

孙悟空恳求⑦师父："您再给我一次机会吧。"

师父摇摇头说："以后⑧，不可以跟别人说我是你的师父，记住⑨了吗？"

① 钟 (zhōng) *n.*
clock, bell
e.g., 大钟敲了三下。

② 三更 (sāngēng) *n.*
midnight
e.g., 半夜三更，你出去干什么？

③ 面前 (miànqián) *n.*
presence
e.g., 他在她面前突然变得很害羞。

④ 炫耀 (xuànyào) *v.*
show off, flaunt
e.g., 他到处炫耀自己的学问。

⑤ 张扬 (zhāngyáng) *v.* show off, make known
e.g., 他是个张扬的人。

⑥ 惹祸 (rěhuò) *v.*
make trouble
e.g., 这个男孩儿总在外面惹祸。

⑦ 恳求 (kěnqiú) *v.*
beg sincerely, implore
e.g., 他恳求我别走。

⑧ 以后 (yǐhòu) *n.*
afterwards
e.g., 以后你就会明白的。

⑨ 记住 (jìzhù) *v.*
remember, bear in mind
e.g., 你一定要记住我的话。

<u>孙悟空</u>点点头，伤心地走了。

[1] 七十二变（qīshí'èrbiàn）：72 Methods of Transformation
菩提祖师教孙悟空的本领之一。"变"指变化，而七十二是个虚数，意思是多，七十二变是指很多种变化。而这种变化既可以使自己变，也可以变别的东西。One of the skills taught by Subhuti to Monkey King. It is a type of esoteric knowledge which allows the user to transform themselves and others into different beings. Here, the number 72 is used to mean "many", and does not reference the actual number 72 or any real numerical value.

[2] 筋斗云（jīndǒuyún）：Somersault Cloud
孙悟空飞行时所乘之云，一个筋斗便能行十万八千里。The cloud that Monkey King rides on to do a somersault. He can travel 108,000 *li* (or 54,000 km) in a single somersault.

思考题：
Answer the following questions according to the story.

1. 美猴王为什么想去学习本领？

2. 孙悟空跟着师父学习了哪些本领？

3. 师父为什么要赶孙悟空走？

3．借宝贝，闯<u>龙宫</u>

主要人物和地点：
Main Characters and Places

龙王（lóngwáng）：《西游记》中主要有四位龙王——东海龙王、西海龙王、南海龙王和北海龙王，他们住在各自的龙宫里，能行云布雨、消灾降福，象征祥瑞。孙悟空的金箍棒是在东海龙王那儿拿的，白龙马是西海龙王的儿子。

Dragon King: There are four dragon kings in the novel, including Dragon King of the East Sea, Dragon King of the West Sea, Dragon King of the South Sea and Dragon King of the North Sea. They live in different dragon palaces. They symbolize auspiciousness because they are capable of producing clouds and rain, preventing disasters and bringing fortune. Monkey King obtains his Gold-banded Cudgel from Dragon King of the East Sea. White Dragon Horse is the son of Dragon King of the West Sea.

玉帝（Yùdì）：众神中地位最高的神，相当于天上的皇帝。他除了统领天上的神仙外，还管理宇宙万物的兴隆衰败，是道教中的神仙形象。

Jade Emperor: The emperor in heaven who ranks as the highest among all celestial beings. Apart from being a commander of heaven, he takes charge of the revival and decline of all the beings in the universe. He is one of the immortals in Taoist beliefs.

龙宫（lónggōng）：中国古代神话传说中龙王的宫殿。

Dragon Palace: According to traditional Chinese myths, it refers to a royal palace where a dragon king lives.

① 惊 (jīng) *u* be shocked, be stunned
e.g., 她看见我，惊叫了一声。

② 兵器 (bīngqì) *n.* weapon
e.g., 这件兵器很厉害。

③ 斤 (jīn) *m.w. jīn*, a unit for measuring weight equaling 0.5 kilograms
e.g., 我买了一斤苹果。

孙悟空回到花果山后，大家都很高兴。它给大家表演了自己的本领，猴子们都惊①呆了。

孙悟空说："可惜我没有好的兵器②。"

老猴子说："您可以去龙宫找找。"

孙悟空高兴地说："太好了！我现在就去。"

龙王听说孙悟空很厉害，不敢拒绝他。他拿出很多兵器，让孙悟空选择。孙悟空举起一件三千六百斤③的兵器，说："太轻太轻。"

龙王又让人抬出一件七千多斤重的，孙悟空说："还是太轻。"

龙王说："没有更重的了，您去别的地方找吧。"

孙悟空坐下来，笑着说："如果拿不出我满意的，我就不走了。"

龙王说："好吧。还有一件，你要是拿得动^①，就送你了。"

他们来到海底，龙王指着一个大柱子^②说："就是它。"

孙悟空使劲儿搬了一下，没搬动。又试了几次，还是没搬动。他擦擦汗，说："这个宝贝太大了，要是小一点儿就好了。"大柱子好像能听懂他的话，真的变小了。

孙悟空说："再小一点儿。"于是它又小了点儿。孙悟空把它拿起来，看见上面有字：如意金箍棒¹，

① 动 (dòng) *v.* move
e.g., 你不要动我的东西。
② 柱子 (zhùzi) *n.* pillar
e.g., 这根柱子真粗。

一万三千五百斤。

得到满意的兵器后，孙悟空又让龙王送他一套战袍①。

龙王不高兴地说："没有。"

孙悟空举起金箍棒，说："没有？那就不要怪②我了。"

龙王吓得赶紧说："有，有。我马上就给您送来。"

于是，孙悟空拿着金箍棒，穿着漂亮的战袍，高兴地回花果山了。孙悟空刚走，龙王就去玉帝那里告状③了。

① 战袍 (zhànpáo) *n.* war robe
e.g.,这件战袍真漂亮。

② 怪 (guài) *v.* blame
e.g.,你别怪她，她不是故意的。

③ 告状 (gàozhuàng) *v.* lodge a complaint against someone
e.g.,他又去老师那里告状了。

[1] 金箍棒（jīngūbàng）：Gold-banded Cudgel

它两头是两个金箍，中间是一段乌铁，紧挨着金箍有镌刻的一行字，写着"如意金箍棒，一万三千五百斤"，是太上老君所造。An iron cudgel with two gold bands on both ends. The cudgel is inscribed with the following characters 如意金箍棒，一万三千五百斤 (As-you-will Gold-banded Cudgel, weighing 6,750 kg.) It was made by the Grand Supreme Elderly Lord in Chinese mythology.

思考题：

Answer the following questions according to the story.

1. 孙悟空去哪里借兵器了？

2. 他借到了什么兵器？

3. 龙王愿意把兵器借给孙悟空吗？为什么？

4. 大闹① 天宫

主要人物和地点：
Main Characters and Places

太白金星（Tàibái Jīnxīng）：中国民间信仰和道教神仙中知名度最高的神之一，他忠厚善良，主要职务是玉皇大帝的特使，负责传达各种命令，受到人们的喜爱。

Planet Venus: One of the most renowned deities in Chinese folklore and Taoism. He is honest and kind-hearted and mainly acts as the special envoy of Jade Emperor for transmitting various orders. Therefore, he is popular among the public.

王母娘娘（Wángmǔ Niángniang）：天上所有仙女的领袖，是天宫里地位最高的女神。她掌管蟠桃园，里面的桃子具有使人长生不老的功效。

Queen Mother of Western Heaven: As the head of all the fairy maidens, she ranks the highest among all the goddesses in the Heavenly Palace. She is in charge of the Heavenly Peach Garden which produces peaches that can make people live forever and never grow old.

太上老君（Tàishàng Lǎojūn）：道教中一位法力高强的神仙，他懂得炼丹之术，还有许多厉害的宝物，如金刚镯、红葫芦等。他曾经为了降服孙悟空，将其放入炼丹炉中，却使孙悟空获得了一双可以分辨出妖怪的火眼金睛，这在取经路上起了很大作用。

Grand Supreme Elderly Lord: A powerful immortal in Taoism. He knows how to distill elixirs and possesses many treasures, such as the Diamond Bracelet, Crimson Gourd and others. In order to subdue Monkey King, he puts him in his furnace used for distilling elixirs. Beyond his expectations, Monkey King comes out with a pair of golden-gaze fiery eyes, which allows him to distinguish demons. This ability helps them a lot during the journey.

天宫（tiāngōng）：中国传说中玉帝、神仙居住的宫殿。
Heavenly Palace: According to the Chinese legend, it is a royal
palace where Jade Emperor and other immortals live.

蟠桃园（Pántáo Yuán）：园内共有三千三百三十三棵蟠桃
树。蟠桃树依次每三千年开花，三千年结果，三千年成
熟。传说，蟠桃园中的仙果凡人吃了便可以长生不老，得
道成仙；神仙吃了法力无边。
Heavenly Peach Garden: There are 3,333 peach trees in the
garden. The trees bloom every 3,000 years, and it takes
another 3,000 years for them to yield fruit, and then another
3,000 years for the fruits to ripen. Legend has it that this
magic fruit, if eaten by mortals, will bring eternal life to them
and make them become immortals; when eaten by immortals,
it can bestow omnipotent magical power.

① 闹 (nào) *v.* stir up trouble, cause chaos
e.g., 孩子一直闹，妈妈也没办法。

孙悟空不但在龙宫里惹了祸，还到了阎王¹那里，把自己和其他猴子的名字从生死簿²上划掉了。只要名字从生死簿上划掉，他们就不会死了。

阎王和龙王都来找玉帝，玉帝非常生气。

太白金星建议说："让孙悟空在天宫做个小官，他就不会到处惹祸了。"

于是玉帝安排孙悟空做了个养①马的小官。

孙悟空高兴极了，他对猴子们说："玉帝请我去天宫做大官啦！"

有一天，孙悟空问其他神仙："我的官大不大？"

大家都说："不大，不大，是最小的。"

① 养 (yǎng) v. raise, keep, grow
e.g., 我喜欢养狗。

① 气 (qì) *v.* become angry
e.g., 他气得脸都白了。

② 飞 (fēi) *v.* fly
e.g., 一只鸟在天上飞。

③ 特意 (tèyì) *adv.* on purpose, specially
e.g., 我是特意来看你的。

④ 只不过 (zhǐbuguò) *adv.* only, just
e.g., 他只不过是个孩子。

⑤ 虚名 (xūmíng) *n.* title carrying no privilege, undeserved name
e.g., 那只是虚名，其实他根本没有那么厉害。

⑥ 而已 (éryǐ) *interj.* that's all, nothing more, just
e.g., 才批评了你两句而已，你就不高兴了。

⑦ 仙女 (xiānnǚ) *n.* fairy maiden
e.g., 你相信世界上有仙女吗？

孙悟空听了，气①得飞②回了花果山。他为了气玉帝，特意③给自己取了一个新名字——齐天大圣³！

这次，玉帝更生气了，他派了很多人去花果山把孙悟空抓回来。可是这些人都打不过孙悟空。

太白金星又建议说："不如就让他做'齐天大圣'，只不过④是个虚名⑤而已⑥。只要他不再惹祸就行了。"于是，孙悟空高兴地回了天宫。这次，他被派去管理蟠桃园，吃了那里的桃可以长生不老。

孙悟空就喜欢吃桃。每次饿了，他都摘蟠桃园里的大桃来吃。直到有一天，王母娘娘要举办宴会，仙女⑦

① 办 (bàn) *v.* host, hold
e.g., 我准备办一个晚会，你来参加吗?

② 迷迷糊糊 (mímí hūhū) in a daze.
e.g., 他喝多了，迷迷糊糊的。

③ 仙丹 (xiāndān) *n.* elixir
e.g., 传说中，道士会炼仙丹。

们才发现，大桃都没了。

孙悟空问仙女们："宴会请了谁?"

一位仙女说："几乎请了所有的神仙。"

孙悟空又问："有没有请齐天大圣?"

仙女们摇摇头，说："没听过这个名字。"

孙悟空生气地说："请了所有人都不请我，我让你们办①不成宴会!"

他趁神仙们还没有到，偷偷跑到宴会上，又吃又喝。吃饱后，他又迷迷糊糊②地跑到太上老君那里，趁没人看着，把仙丹③都吃了。

孙悟空知道自己惹了祸，于是又飞回花果山了。

23

[1] 阎王（Yánwáng）：Yama
统领阴间的神，审判人生前的行为并给予相应的惩罚。The god ruling the netherworld. He conducts trials on people's bad behavior during their lifetime and then brings due punishment to them.

[2] 生死簿（shēngsǐbù）：Life-and-death Book
中国古代神话中可以定人生死的书簿。The book that determines a person's life and death in ancient mythology.

[3] 齐天大圣（Qítiān Dàshèng）：Great Sage Equal to Heaven
孙悟空给自己想的一个名字，意思是与天同齐，与玉帝比肩。A name created by Monkey King for himself, which means he is the equal of heaven and Jade Emperor.

思考题：
Answer the following questions according to the story.

1. 孙悟空为什么自称"齐天大圣"？

2. 孙悟空在天宫闯了什么祸？

3. 孙悟空闯祸后去了哪里？

5. 被困五行山

主要人物和地点：
Main Characters and Places

二郎神（Èrlángshén）：本名杨戬，是仙女和凡人所生，是玉帝的外甥。他力大无穷，武艺高强，额间长了第三只慧眼，还有一只哮天犬跟随左右。在孙悟空大闹天宫时，他曾和其他神仙一起，将孙悟空抓了起来。

God Erlang: His original name is Yang Jian. He is the son of a fairy maiden and a human, and the nephew of Jade Emperor. He has great strength and is skilled at martial arts. He has three magical eyes on his head and a heavenly dog that follows him. When Monkey King causes havoc in the Heavenly Palace, God Erlang catches Monkey King with the other immortals.

如来佛祖（Rúlái Fózǔ）：如来佛祖的原型是释迦牟尼，住在西天大雷音寺，是一位法力无边、至高无上的佛祖。在孙悟空大闹天宫、所有天兵天将都被打败之时，是如来佛祖及时出手相救，将孙悟空压在了五行山下。后他又选择了唐僧去西天取经，普渡众生。

The Buddha: He originates from Buddha Shakyamuni, who lives at Great Leiyin Temple in Western Heaven. He enjoys supremacy with omnipotent powers. Monkey King at one time creates a tremendous uproar in the Heavenly Palace. When no soldiers from heaven can defeat him, it's the Buddha who helps the situation and traps Monkey King under the Five Elements Mountain. Later, he picks Monk Xuanzang to go west in search of the Buddhist scriptures in order to enlignten the masses.

五行山（Wǔxíng Shān）：为了压制孙悟空，佛祖用五指化作一座大山，将孙悟空压在山下。

Five Elements Mountain: In order to subdue Monkey King, the Buddha turned his five fingers into a towering mountain to imprison him.

① 烧 (shāo) *v.* burn e.g., 小心，别把水烧干了。

玉帝知道孙悟空做的事情后，非常生气，派了天兵天将[1]去抓他。可是孙悟空太厉害了，把天兵天将都打败了，于是玉帝又派了二郎神去。

二郎神果然厉害，两个人打了很久，也分不出输赢。就在这时候，太上老君趁孙悟空不注意，用金刚镯[2]从背后打了孙悟空，终于把他抓住了。

可是无论用什么方法，都杀不死孙悟空。太上老君说："把他放进八卦炉[3]，用火烧①死他。"于是孙悟空又被扔进了八卦炉里。

八卦炉里的火越烧越大，到了第四十九天，火已经烧到最大。太上老君说：

齐天大圣到此一游

① 打赌 (dǎdǔ) v. bet
e.g., 我跟他打了个赌。

② 手掌 (shǒuzhǎng)
n. palm
e.g., 他的手掌真大。

"可以打开了。"

就在八卦炉打开的时候，孙悟空突然从里面跳了出来！他不但没死，反而有了"火眼金睛[4]"。他举起金箍棒大声喊："玉帝，快把天宫让给我！"玉帝赶快派人去请如来佛祖。

如来佛祖跟孙悟空打了个赌①："如果你能翻出我的手掌②，就让你当玉帝，怎么样？"

孙悟空高兴地说："你不要后悔啊。"说完，他就跳到了佛祖的手掌上。

翻了几个筋斗云后，孙悟空看见了五根大柱子。他想："我翻一个筋斗云就能飞十万八千里，现在应该是到天的尽头了，这些一定是用来支撑天的柱子。"

于是，他在这些柱子上写了几个字，来证明自己到过这里。写完，他又跳回到佛祖的手掌上。

孙悟空说："我已经飞到天的尽头了，还在柱子上写了字。"

佛祖摇摇头说："那不是天的尽头，那只是我的手指。你看！"

果然，孙悟空写的字就在佛祖的手指上。

孙悟空生气地说："我不相信，我要再去看看。"

这时候，佛祖突然把手掌翻过来，变成了一座大山，把孙悟空压①住了。佛祖又在山顶贴②了一张符③。

① 压 (yā) *v.* press, weigh down
e.g., 书下面压的是什么？

② 贴 (tiē) *v.* stick to, paste
e.g., 墙上贴着一张画儿。

③ 符 (fú) *n.* talisman, magical figures drawn to invoke or expel spirits and bring good or ill fortune
e.g., 那个道士给他画了一张符。

从此，<u>孙悟空</u>就被压在了这座五行山下。

[1] 天兵天将（tiānbīng tiānjiàng）：Celestial Soldiers
中国神话中天神的兵将。The soldiers commanded by the gods of heaven in the Chinese mythology.

[2] 金刚镯（jīngāngzhuó）：Diamond Bracelet
太上老君的众多法宝之一，水火不侵，能收取各种宝物。One of the Grand Supreme Elderly Lord's magical objects. It cannot be ruined by either fire or water and can be used to seize a variety of magical objects.

[3] 八卦炉（bāguàlú）：Eight-way Trigram Furnace
太上老君炼丹制宝时所用的宝物，里面的火是四大天火之一，非常厉害。A treasured utensil used by the Grand Supreme Elderly Lord to distill pellets for eternal life. The fire inside, one of the four types of heavenly fire, is very powerful.

[4] 火眼金睛（huǒyǎn-jīnjīng）：Fiery Eyes with Golden Pupils
孙悟空被烧后的意外收获，有了火眼金睛，可以认出妖怪。With his eyes sharpened after being burned in the furnace, an unexpected benefit of his punishment, Monkey King is able to recognize evil spirits in any form.

思考题：
Answer the following questions according to the story.

1. 天兵天将失败后，玉帝又派了谁去抓孙悟空？

2. 太上老君想用什么方法杀死孙悟空？

3. 最后是谁制服了孙悟空？

6. 唐僧收徒弟 [1]

主要人物和地点：
Main Characters and Places

唐僧（Tángsēng）：又叫玄奘，是唐朝的一位高僧。他心地仁慈，个性执着而坚韧，一心想着取得佛经，教化百姓。尽管他在取经的路上经历了很多困难，但他还是坚持不放弃，终于在三个徒弟的保护下，到达了西天，取得佛经。

Monk Tang: An eminent monk in the Tang Dynasty (618-907), also known as Monk Xuanzang. He is benevolent, persistent and tenacious. His greatest purpose is to acquire the Buddhist scriptures and enlighten the public. Even though he encounters numerous obstacles during the journey, he never gives up and finally acquires the scriptures in Western Heaven with the help of his three disciples.

观音菩萨（Guānyīn Púsa）：佛教中慈悲和智慧的象征。她法力高深，当众生遇到困难和苦痛，她都能及时救护。她点化了孙悟空、猪八戒、沙和尚成为唐僧的徒弟，又在他们取经的路上屡次帮助他们化险为夷。

Guanyin Bodhisattva: In Buddhism, she represents mercy and wisdom. She is powerful and able to rescue the masses whenever they encounter hardships. She converts Monkey King, Monk Pig and Monk Sand into Monk Xuanzang's disciples. In addition, she helps with numerous dangers on their way to Western Heaven.

[1] 徒弟 (túdì) *n.* apprentice, disciple
e.g., 我是他的徒弟。

① 佛经 (fójīng) *n.*
Buddhist scriptures
e.g., 那个寺庙里有
很多佛经。

② 传 (chuán) *v.* pass
on (knowledge, skill,
etc.)
e.g., 师傅把所有本
领都传给了徒弟。

③ 法术 (fǎshù) *n.*
magic power
e.g., 他是个有法术
的人。

④ 和尚 (héshang) *n.*
monk
e.g., 和尚不许吃肉。

⑤ 袈裟 (jiāshā) *n.* a
patchwork outer
vestment worn by a
Buddhist monk
e.g., 这件袈裟是送
给那位师傅的。

⑥ 锡杖 (xīzhàng) *n.*
monk's cane with a
tin ring or rings at
the head
e.g., 这根锡杖真漂亮。

如来佛祖有佛经①要传②，可他要找一个不会法术③的普通人，经过很多困难，到西天¹去取才可以。于是，观音菩萨来到大唐²，为佛祖找那个人。

观音菩萨刚到大唐，就遇到一位叫玄奘的和尚④在讲佛经。菩萨听了，觉得他就是佛祖要找的那个人。

于是观音菩萨对玄奘说："在西天有更好的佛经，你愿意去取吗？"

玄奘高兴地回答："愿意，愿意。"

菩萨把佛祖给的袈裟⑤和锡杖⑥都交给了玄奘。玄奘骑着一匹白马，向西天出发了。因为玄奘是唐朝的僧人，所以后人都叫他唐僧。

① 手 (shǒu) *n.* hand
e.g., 他手里拿着一本书。

② 露 (lù) *v.* expose
e.g., 她的脸上露出了笑容。

③ 轰 (hōng) *onom.*
bang, boom
e.g., 轰！炸弹爆炸了。

④ 声 (shēng) *n.*
sound
e.g., 远处传来一声大叫。

唐僧走到一座山下，突然听到有人喊："师父救我。"

唐僧小心地走过去，看见一只猴子，整个身体都被压在山下，只有头和手①还露②在外面。原来他就是五百年前被佛祖压在山下的孙悟空。

孙悟空看见唐僧，高兴地喊："师父救我！观音菩萨让我给您当徒弟，保护您去取佛经。"

唐僧问："我怎么救你？"

"山顶上有一张符，您把它撕下来就行了。"孙悟空向上指了指。

唐僧撕下了符，孙悟空又说："您走远点儿。"

唐僧赶紧退到很远的地方，"轰"③的一声④，五行山倒了。孙悟空出来了，成了唐僧的第一个徒弟。

路上，一伙^①强盗^②突然出现，孙悟空拿出金箍棒，把他们都打死了。

唐僧生气地说："你怎么可以杀人？"

"我为了保护你才杀人。你不感谢我，还教训我。我不去西天了。"说完，孙悟空就飞走了。

唐僧一个人走着走着，遇到了一个老妇人^③。老妇人送给他一个帽子，并对他说："你把帽子给你徒弟戴上。我再教你一个咒语^④，他再不听话^⑤你就念。"

这个老妇人就是观音菩萨变的。

① 伙 (huǒ) m.w.
group, crowd
e.g., 那里有一伙人。

② 强盗 (qiángdào) n.
bandit
e.g., 那伙强盗被警察抓了。

③ 老妇人 (lǎofùrén)
n. old lady
e.g., 那个老妇人是谁？

④ 咒语 (zhòuyǔ) n.
incantation, spell
e.g., 她在念咒语。

⑤ 听话 (tīnghuà) v.
be obedient
e.g., 他是个听话的孩子。

[1] 西天（xītiān）：Western Heaven
中国古代对印度的称谓。因为印度在中国西南方向，故略称西天。所谓
"西天取经"即指去印度取经。A name used by ancient Chinese to refer
to ancient India. Since India was located to the southwest of China, it was
called Western Heaven for short. "Obtaining Buddhist scriptures from
Western Heaven" means obtaining the scriptures from ancient India.

[2] 大唐（Dàtáng）：Great Tang (Empire)
唐朝的别称。Also called the Tang Dynasty (618-907).

思考题：
Answer the following questions according to the story.

1. 观音菩萨找了谁去西天取佛经？

2. 唐僧是怎么救出孙悟空的？

3. 唐僧用了什么办法让孙悟空听自己的话？

7. 收服 ^① <u>白龙马</u>

主要人物和地点：
Main Characters and Places

白龙马（Báilóngmǎ）：西海龙王三太子，因触犯天条要被斩首。后观音菩萨出面才免于死罪，被贬到蛇盘山等待唐僧取经。之后他又误吃唐僧所骑的白马，于是变身为白龙马，载乘唐僧上西天取经，最终修成正果。

White Dragon Horse: He is the third son of the Dragon King of the West Sea. He is sentenced to be beheaded for breaching heavenly rules. With the help of Guanyin Bodhisattva, he is excused from the death penalty. Instead, he is exiled to the Snake Winding Mountain to wait for Monk Xuanzang to come. Afterwards, he eats Monk Xuanzang's horse by mistake, and thus is transformed into a white dragon horse. He has to carry Monk Xuanzang to Western Heaven in search of Buddhist scriptures. In the end, he finds fulfillment and becomes an immortal.

---

① 收服 (shōufú) *v.* bring under control
e.g., 皇帝把那片土地上的人民收服了。

① 金箍 (jīngū) *n.* gold ring, gold hoop e.g., 那条金箍紧紧地套在他的头上。

没过多久，孙悟空就回来了。他看唐僧不但没有生气，反而送给他一个帽子，高高兴兴地就把帽子戴上了。

唐僧看他把帽子戴上，就念起紧箍咒[1]来。

孙悟空突然觉得头疼，一边喊疼，一边使劲儿拉帽子，想把它摘掉。帽子被摘掉了，可是却留了一个金箍①在头上。

这时候，他才发现是师父在旁边念咒语。

孙悟空请求唐僧说："师父，别念了！我知道错了。"

唐僧说："以后你不能再乱杀人了。"

孙悟空连忙点头答应："不敢了，不敢了。您把这

40

① 钻 (zuān) *v.* get into, go through e.g., 那个小孩钻进了山洞里。

② 见 (jiàn) *v.* see e.g., 东西刚才还在这儿，怎么不见了呢？

③ 犯 (fàn) *v.* commit (a crime), make (a mistake) e.g., 他不敢把犯的错告诉妈妈。

金箍摘掉吧。"

唐僧说："这是观音菩萨给的，我也摘不掉。"

于是，孙悟空只好跟着唐僧继续出发了。

一天，他们来到一个瀑布前，突然从瀑布里钻① 出一条白龙，一口就把唐僧的马吃了。孙悟空生气极了，举起金箍棒就向它打去。白龙打不过孙悟空，于是又钻进瀑布里不见② 了。

有人告诉孙悟空，白龙是观音菩萨放到这里来的。孙悟空听了，就赶紧去找观音菩萨。

观音菩萨对孙悟空说："那白龙是龙王的儿子，因为犯③ 了大错，要被杀死。我看他可怜，就把它放到那条瀑布里，让他跟着你们一起去西天。"

孙悟空不高兴地说："他都把马吃了，让我们怎么去西天？"

观音菩萨笑着回答："你跟着我来，我自然有办法。"

观音菩萨来到瀑布前，对着瀑布喊："小白龙出来，你师父已经到了。"白龙听了，赶紧从瀑布中钻了出来，跪^①在地上。

观音菩萨说了一声"变"，白龙就变成了一匹漂亮的白马。

于是，唐僧骑着白马，和孙悟空继续向西天走去。

① 跪 (guì) *v.* kneel, go down on one's knees
e.g., 他跪在地上请求她原谅。

[1] 紧箍咒（jǐngūzhòu）：Ring Tightening Mantra
唐僧用来制服孙悟空的咒语，能使孙悟空头上的金箍收缩，头痛欲裂。后用来比喻束缚人的东西。The mantra chanted by Monk Xuanzang to control Monkey King. When Monk Xuanzang chants the mantra, the gold ring on Monkey King's head shrinks to cause an unbearable headache. Later, it is used metaphorically to indicate the things that constrain or restrict people's mind.

思考题：
Answer the following questions according to the story.

1. 谁把唐僧的马吃了？

2. 观音菩萨为什么把小白龙放在瀑布里？

3. 小白龙最后变成了什么？

8. 夸宝贝，丢袈裟

主要人物和地点：
Main Characters and Places

黑风怪（Hēifēngguài）：原是一头黑熊，住在黑风山黑风洞，修行多年成为妖怪，使一柄黑缨长枪，善于变化，手段也很厉害。

Black Wind Demon: At one time a black bear who lived in the Black Wind Cave on the Black Wind Mountain. After years of practicing austerity, it turned into a demon, who mastered a lot of powerful tactics and was adept at changing fighting styles by using a black-tasselled spear.

① 间 (jiān) *m.w.*
(used for rooms)
e.g., 这间屋子很大。

② 寺庙 (sìmiào) *n.*
temple
e.g., 寺庙里住着很
多和尚。

③ 珍贵 (zhēnguì) *adj.*
precious, valuable
e.g., 这真是件珍贵
的礼物。

④ 收集 (shōují) *v.*
collect, gather
e.g., 他喜欢收集老
照片。

⑤ 各种各样 (gè
zhǒng gè yàng) *adj.*
various, all kinds of
e.g., 他准备了各种
各样的食物。

有一天，唐僧和孙悟空来到一间①寺庙②休息。

管理这间寺庙的人是一个老和尚，他请唐僧坐下，让小和尚给唐僧倒茶。

"真是好茶，谢谢您。"唐僧笑着说。

老和尚回答："哪里，哪里，我这小地方怎么能跟大唐比呢？您从那里来，一定有很多珍贵③的宝贝吧？能不能拿出来让我们看看呢？"

原来，这老和尚有一个爱好，就是喜欢收集④各种各样⑤的宝贝。

唐僧没有说话。可是孙悟空却着急地回答："当然有！"说完，就把观音菩萨送的袈裟拿了出来。

老和尚从来没看过这

么[1]好的袈裟，一边小心地摸着，一边说："好宝贝，真是好宝贝啊！今天晚上可不可以把袈裟借给我，让我好好看看呢？"

孙悟空痛快地答应了，可是唐僧却担心地对孙悟空说："那是观音菩萨给的，如果弄丢了，怎么办呢？"

孙悟空回答说："师父您放心，明天早上我就把袈裟要回来。"

老和尚太喜欢这袈裟了，他看了又看，摸了又摸，实在不想把袈裟再还回去，于是，他想了一个办法。

夜里，唐僧睡着[2]了，孙悟空听到外面有人说话："把火点上。"原来老和尚想把他们烧死。

① 这么 (zhème) adv.
so, such
e.g., 今天这么冷，
你就别出去了。

② 睡着 (shuìzháo) v.
fall asleep
e.g., 他很快就睡着了。

47

孙悟空没有叫醒师父，他向神仙借了一个避火罩[1]，把唐僧住的房间盖住了。火越来越大，结果把整个寺庙都点着了。

寺庙的后面有一座山，山上住着一个黑风怪。他趁大家不注意的时候，悄悄进了老和尚的房间，把袈裟偷走了。

好不容易弄到的袈裟不见了，寺庙也被烧了，老和尚越想越伤心，最后往墙上一撞，死了。

[1] 避火罩（bìhuǒzhào）：Fire Proof Shield
孙悟空向一个神仙借的法宝，只要罩上，就可以避开火的侵袭。A magic weapon Monkey King borrowed from an immortal. When something is covered by the shield, fire cannot affect it.

思考题：
Answer the following questions according to the story.

1. 老和尚为什么想烧死唐僧和孙悟空？
2. 是谁把袈裟偷走了？
3. 老和尚为什么要自杀？

9. 智斗^① 黑风怪

① 智斗 (zhìdòu) v.
fight with wisdom
e.g., 这是一个警察
智斗小偷的故事。

老和尚死了，孙悟空就问小和尚们袈裟在哪儿，可是他们都说不知道。孙悟空想了一会儿，又问："这附近有没有妖怪？"

一个和尚回答说："后面山上有一个黑风怪。"

"你们照顾好我师父，我现在就去找黑风怪。"说完，孙悟空就走了。

孙悟空来到黑风怪住的山洞，在洞口大声喊："黑风怪，快把我师父的袈裟交出来！"

黑风怪听了，拿着兵器就冲了出来。可是，他根本打不过孙悟空，没过多久，就逃回山洞里了。这次，无论孙悟空怎么骂他，他都不

① 道士 (dàoshi) *n.*
Taoist priest
e.g., 这里住着一个
老道士。

② 端 (duān) *v.* carry,
hold something level
with both hands
e.g., 你给客人端杯水。

出来了。没办法，孙悟空只好去找观音菩萨帮忙，观音菩萨答应帮忙，并跟孙悟空来到了黑风怪住的地方。

他们刚要跟孙悟空进山洞，就看见一个道士①端②着盘子走了过来，盘子里装了两颗仙丹。孙悟空看出那个道士是妖怪变的，于是把他打死了。观音菩萨变成了这个道士，孙悟空变成了一颗仙丹。

观音菩萨变的道士走进山洞，把仙丹递给黑风怪，说："这颗仙丹是为您准备的，吃了它您就可以长生不老了……"还没有说完，黑风怪就把仙丹抢过去吃了。

孙悟空进了黑风怪的肚子里，又打又跳。黑风怪疼得受不了，赶紧请求说："我错了，我错了，我再也不敢偷您的袈裟了，求^①您出来吧。"

黑风怪把袈裟交给了<u>观音菩萨</u>。<u>观音菩萨</u>拿出一个金箍，套在了<u>黑风怪</u>的脑袋上。

<u>孙悟空</u>刚从<u>黑风怪</u>的肚子里出来，他就要打<u>孙悟空</u>。这时候，<u>观音菩萨</u>开始念咒语，<u>黑风怪</u>脑袋上的金箍越来越紧^②，疼得他赶紧认错^③。

袈裟拿回来了，<u>唐僧</u>和<u>孙悟空</u>离开了寺庙，又继续向西出发了。

① 求 (qiú) *v.* beg
e.g., 她求我不要把这件事告诉别人。

② 紧 (jǐn) *adj.* tight
e.g., 这条裤子太紧了。

③ 认错 (rèncuò) *v.* admit a mistake, make an apology
e.g., 孩子向妈妈认错，妈妈原谅了他。

思考题：
Answer the following questions according to the story.

1. 孙悟空找谁帮忙收服黑风怪？

2. 孙悟空是怎么进到黑风怪肚子里的？

3. 最后袈裟有没有要回来？

10. <u>高老庄</u>收服<u>猪八戒</u>

主要人物和地点：
Main Characters and Places

猪八戒（Zhū Bājiè）：原来是天宫上的天蓬元帅，因为犯错被贬下凡，错投猪胎，嘴脸与猪相似。他虽然懒惰、贪吃又好色，但也憨厚善良。他使用的兵器是九齿钉钯，本领虽不及孙悟空，但在取经的路上也出了不少力，是唐僧的二徒弟。

Zhu Bajie (Monk Pig): He used to be the Marshal of the Heavenly Canopy at the Heavenly Palace, but is exiled to the mortal world for his wrongdoings. He is accidentally reincarnated as a pig, so he ends up looking like one. Though lazy, gluttonous and lustful, he is also simple, honest and kind-hearted. His weapon is the Nine-tooth Rake. His martial arts skills are not as good as Monkey King, but he contributes a lot on the journey. He is the second disciple of Monk Xuanzang.

嫦娥（Cháng'é）：月宫里一个漂亮的仙女。
Chang'e: A beautiful fairy living in the Moon Palace.

高老庄（Gāolǎo Zhuāng）：地名。
Gao's Village: Place name.

53

一天，唐僧和孙悟空走到了一个叫高老庄的地方。

几个月以前，这里来了一个姓猪的人，长得又高又壮①，高老庄的主人高太公很喜欢他，于是就把小女儿嫁给了他。可是有一天，他喝醉了，居然变成了一个长着猪脑袋、人身体的妖怪，大家都吓坏了。高太公想赶他走，可是他就是不走，还把高太公的小女儿锁在了房间里。孙悟空了解了情况，就跟高太公说："我一定能抓住那个妖怪。"

妖怪不在家的时候，孙悟空把高太公的小女儿救了出来，然后自己变成她的样子，等妖怪回来。

过了一会儿，妖怪回来

① 壮 (zhuàng) *adj.* strong
e.g., 他是个很壮的男孩子。

① 当年 (dāngnián) *n.*
at that time, then
e.g., 当年，你还是
个小女孩呢。

② 欺负 (qīfu) *v.* bully
e.g., 你以后不许再欺
负你弟弟了。

③ 调戏 (tiáoxì) *v.* flirt
with
e.g., 他因为调戏妇
女被抓了起来。

了。他一边走一边喊："老婆，老婆，我回来啦。"孙悟空举起金箍棒就打，吓得妖怪赶紧跑了出去。

孙悟空变回了原来的样子，说："你看我是谁！"

妖怪一看，原来是孙悟空，赶紧拿出兵器和孙悟空打了起来。他一边打一边生气地说："你当年①在天宫上闹了一场，今天又来欺负②我。"原来，这个妖怪以前是个神仙，有一天喝醉了，调戏③了嫦娥。玉帝知道了很生气，就把他变成了猪的样子。

妖怪打不过孙悟空就跑了，孙悟空追到一个山洞，妖怪突然消失了。孙悟空打破了山洞的门，冲了进去。

妖怪生气地问："是高太公把你找来的？"

孙悟空回答："观音菩萨叫我保护唐僧去取佛经，经过高老庄，正好遇到了你这个妖怪！"

妖怪听了，放下兵器，说："别打了。我也是观音菩萨派来的。"

从此，这个妖怪就成了唐僧的二徒弟，叫猪八戒。

思考题：
Answer the following questions according to the story.

1. 高太公为什么要找人抓妖怪？
2. 妖怪为什么被变成了猪的样子？
3. 唐僧的二徒弟叫什么？

11. 铲除^①黄风怪

主要人物和地点：
Main Characters and Places

黄风怪（Huángfēngguài）：原是灵山脚下得道的黄毛貂鼠，因为偷吃琉璃盏内的清油，怕被金刚捉拿，便跑到黄风岭占山为王。黄风怪手持一支三股钢叉，神通广大、法力无边，吹出的黄风更是所向无敌。

Yellow Wind Demon: A yellow marten at the foot of Lingshan Mountain who achieved enlightenment by stealing and drinking the oil preserved in a holy glass container. Afterwards, it was so afraid of being caught by the guardians of the Buddha that it ran away to be the lord of the Yellow Wind Ridge. The demon, with its steel trident, has far-reaching supernatural powers. The yellow wind it blows is invincible.

灵吉菩萨（Língjí Púsa）：《西游记》八菩萨之一，住在小须弥山，法力广大，手使飞龙宝杖，并有如来赐给的定风珠等宝贝，多次帮助唐僧师徒取经途中降服妖怪。

Lingji Bodhisattva: One of the eight Bodhisattvas depicted in the novel. He resides in Mount Xiaoxumi (Little Mount Sumeru). He has a Flying-dragon Cane and several other treasures, including a Wind-fixing Pearl bestowed by the Buddha. He helps Monk Xuanzang and his disciples subdue demons several times with his supernatural powers.

---

① 铲除 (chǎnchú) v. eradicate, eliminate
e.g., 他把自己的对手铲除了。

有一天，唐僧和徒弟们走到一座山下，突然刮起大风。这时候，从山上跳出一只老虎，把唐僧抓走了。

孙悟空着急地说："那只老虎一定又是妖怪变的，我们得赶快去山上找师父。"

他们走着走着，来到了一个山洞前。孙悟空觉得这里可能就是妖怪的家。于是，他冲着山洞喊："妖怪，快放了我师父。"

这时候，一个小妖怪走出山洞，一下子就被孙悟空打死了。

孙悟空把死了的小妖怪扔进山洞，对着洞口喊："妖怪，你再不放了我师父，我就把你们都打死。"

原来，抓走唐僧的妖怪

叫"黄风怪"。他听说吃了唐僧肉能长生不老，于是就把唐僧抓了回来。

黄风怪听了孙悟空的话，生气地冲出山洞，跟孙悟空打了起来。孙悟空拔① 下一根毛，用它变出了一百多个孙悟空。他们都拿着金箍棒，朝黄风怪打过去。这时候，黄风怪吹了一口气②，突然刮起一阵大风，把一百多个孙悟空都吹倒了。

黄风怪笑着说："孙悟空也不怎么厉害嘛③。"说完，就又跑进山洞里了。

孙悟空变成一只蜜蜂飞进山洞，找到了被抓的唐僧。

他小声地对唐僧说："师父别害怕，我一定会把

① 拔 (bá) v. pull out
e.g., 我明天去拔牙。

② 气 (qì) n. air, breath
e.g., 听到自己考试通过了，他松了一口气。

③ 嘛 (ma) part. (used to indicate that sth. is obvious)
e.g., 明天我们去爬山，你来不来嘛？

① 爪子 (zhuǎzi) *n.*
claw, paw
e.g., 他被猫的爪子
抓伤了。

② 黄毛鼠
(huángmáoshǔ) *n.*
yellow marten
e.g., 一只黄毛鼠从
洞里钻了出来。

你救出去。"

这时候，他听到黄风怪对小妖怪们说："除了灵吉菩萨，谁都拿我没有办法。"

孙悟空听了，赶紧去找灵吉菩萨帮忙。

灵吉菩萨知道了这件事，赶快拿出飞龙宝杖[1]，和孙悟空一起来到山洞。

小妖怪们赶紧报告黄风怪："孙悟空又来啦！"

黄风怪一点儿也不着急，"害怕什么，一会儿看我怎么收拾他"。

黄风怪走出山洞，又从嘴里吹出大风。这时候，灵吉菩萨的飞龙宝杖变成了一条龙，伸出两只爪子[1]把黄风怪抓住了。黄风怪不见了，出现了一只黄毛鼠[2]，原

来黄风怪是黄毛鼠变的。灵
吉菩萨带走了黄毛鼠，唐僧
他们继续向西天走去。

[1] 飞龙宝杖（fēilóng bǎozhàng）：Flying-dragon Cane
灵吉菩萨的一件法器，作战时可以变作一条金龙，将敌人擒住。
A treasured weapon used by Lingji Bodhisattva which can change into a
golden dragon and be used to subdue demons.

63

思考题：
Answer the following questions according to the story.

1. 黄风怪用什么办法抓走了唐僧？

2. 是谁帮助孙悟空抓住了黄风怪？

3. 黄风怪是什么动物变的？

12. 收服沙和尚

主要人物和地点：
Main Characters and Places

沙和尚（Shā Héshang）：又叫沙僧，原为天宫的卷帘大将，因犯错被贬下凡，成了流沙河里的妖怪，其兵器是降妖宝杖。后来他成为了唐僧的三徒弟。取经路上，他忠心耿耿，任劳任怨，踏踏实实，谨守本分，最终修成正果。

Monk Sand (Sandy): Once a celestial Curtain Lifting General at the Heavenly Palace, also called Monk Sha. Because of a blunder, he is exiled to the mortal world and becomes a demon in the Flowing-sand River. His weapon is the Demon Conquering Shovel. Later, he becomes the third disciple of Monk Xuanzang. On the way to Western Heaven, he is loyal, devoted, dependable and always bears hardships without any complaints. In the end, he returns to the celestial world.

流沙河（Liúshā Hé）：河的名字。
Flowing-sand River: Name of a river.

唐僧和两个徒弟继续向西走。有一天，他们来到了流沙河边。

唐僧看了看这条河，着急地说："这河又宽又深，我恐怕过不去啊。"

就在大家想办法过河的时候，突然从水里跳出一个妖怪，朝唐僧抓去。

孙悟空急忙把师父保护起来。猪八戒冲过去，和妖怪打了起来。孙悟空拿出金箍棒也朝妖怪打去。妖怪看见孙悟空，赶紧跳进了河里。

猪八戒对孙悟空说："我会游泳。我去河里抓妖怪。"

猪八戒跳到河里，又和妖怪打了起来，从水里打到水上，一直打了四个小时。孙悟空着急了，他变成一只鹰①，朝妖怪扑②去。那个妖怪看见孙悟空冲了过来，吓得又跳进水里，再也不出来了。

孙悟空没有办法，只好对唐僧和猪八戒说："师父，我去找观音菩萨帮忙。八戒，你保护师父。"

观音菩萨听了孙悟空的话，说："那个妖怪原来也是天宫的神仙，后来因为犯了错，被贬③到流沙河，做了妖怪。不过他已经被我说服，答应和你们一起，保护唐僧去西天。"

观音菩萨派了一个徒弟，和孙悟空一起回到流沙河。这个徒弟对着河水喊：

66

"快出来吧，你的师父已经来了。"

妖怪听到了，连忙从河里跳了出来。于是，<u>唐僧</u>又收了一个徒弟——<u>沙和尚</u>。

为了帮助大家过河，<u>沙和尚</u>拿出自己的宝贝，变成了一只小船，顺利地带大家过了河。

68

1. 孙悟空去找谁帮忙抓妖怪？

2. 唐僧的第三个徒弟是谁？

3. 唐僧他们是怎么过流沙河的？

① 房子 (fángzi) *n.* house
e.g., 他家的房子真大。

② 并 (bìng) *conj.* and
e.g., 我完全同意并支持你的决定。

③ 饭菜 (fàncài) *n.* meal, food
e.g., 饭菜很香，谢谢你。

13. 猪八戒娶老婆

"都走了一天了，我都要饿死了！那里有个人家，我们去休息一会儿吧。"<u>猪八戒</u>建议说。

<u>唐僧</u>点点头。于是，大家朝那个人家走去。

这个人家的房子^①很大，只有女主人和三个女儿。女主人热情地把大家请进来，并^②准备好了饭菜^③。

大家一边吃，一边听女主人说："三年前我丈夫死了，家里只有女人们了。我觉得你们是好人，不如留下来，做我和女儿们的丈夫吧！"

<u>唐僧</u>没有说话。

<u>猪八戒</u>说："师父，您看她们多可怜，我们就留下

来吧。"

孙悟空笑着说："八戒，你是看女儿们长得漂亮，又有钱，才想留下来吧。"

唐僧生气地说："要留你们留吧！"

八戒看师父生气了，不敢说话了。过了一会儿，他偷偷找到女主人："妈妈，我想娶您的女儿。"

女主人拿出三件衣服，说："这是我女儿们的衣服，你能穿进哪件，就娶哪个。"

八戒高兴地问："如果三件都合适，是不是就能娶三个啊？"

女主人笑笑，没有回答。

猪八戒刚穿上，那衣服就变成了一张网①，把猪八戒绑②了起来。

① 网 (wǎng) *n.* net
e.g., 他用网把鸟捉住了。

② 绑 (bǎng) *v.* tie up
e.g., 他被人绑了起来。

70

唐僧和其他两个徒弟吃完饭，就回房间睡觉了。

第二天早上，唐僧发现自己躺在树林①里，昨天住的房子竟然消失了。

原来女主人和三个女儿是菩萨们变的，想试试他们取佛经的决心。

这时候，树上传来猪八戒的声音："师父，救我！"

孙悟空一边救八戒一边嘲笑②他说："你不是要娶老婆吗？怎么被吊③在了树上？"

猪八戒红着脸说："师父，我错了。"

唐僧原谅了八戒，带着大家继续朝西天走去。

① 树林 (shùlín) n.
woods, forest
e.g., 那片树林真美。

② 嘲笑 (cháoxiào) v.
deride, ridicule
e.g., 不要嘲笑我。

③ 吊 (diào) v.
hang, suspend
e.g., 门前吊着一盏灯笼。

思考题：

Answer the following questions according to the story.

1. 房子的女主人给唐僧提了什么建议？

2. 面对女主人的提议，大家都是怎么做的？

3. 女主人和三个女儿是什么变的？

14. 偷吃^① 人参果 ¹

主要人物和地点：
Main Characters and Places

镇元大仙（Zhènyuán Dàxiān）：一位法力强大的神仙，道号镇元子，住在五庄观，道术深厚精深，连观世音菩萨也让他三分。他种的人参果，九千年成熟一次。闻一闻神奇的人参果，就能活三百六十岁；吃一颗，就能活四万七千年。镇元大仙三绺美髯，貌似童颜。

Immortal Zhenyuan: An immortal with great power. He lives in Wuzhuang Temple and has the Taoist name of Zhenyuanzi. He has such great magic power that even Guanyin Bodhisattva sometimes let him have his own way. The ginseng fruit he grows ripens every 9,000 years. If one smells the fruit, he can live for 360 years. If one eats one, he can live for 47,000 years. He wears three handsome wisps of a beard and looks quite young.

土地神（Tǔdìshén）：土地神是管理一方土地的神仙，是地方行政神，负责保护当地的安宁与平静。

God of Land: A local god who takes charge of a certain area to maintain its peace and stability.

五庄观（Wǔzhuāng Guàn）：镇元大仙住的道观。

Wuzhuang Temple: A Taoist temple where the Immortal Zhenyuan lives.

---

① 偷吃 (tōu chī) *v.* take food sneakily
e.g., 谁偷吃了我的蛋糕？

五庄观里住着一位镇元大仙，他有一棵人参果树，只要吃了人参果就能长生不老。不过，人参果要九千年才能成熟，并且每次树上只长二十八个人参果，非常珍贵。

镇元大仙有事要离开，走前对徒弟说："如果唐僧来了，你们就摘下两个人参果给他吃。"

没过多久，唐僧果然来到五庄观。徒弟们按照师父说的，摘了两个人参果给唐僧。

唐僧看到人参果，吓了一跳："这不是孩子吗？怎么能吃呢？赶快拿走。"

"它只是样子长得像孩子，您放心吃吧。"无论两个徒弟怎么解释，<u>唐僧</u>就是不吃。

于是徒弟们就把人参果拿回去吃了，还笑话<u>唐僧</u>傻。

<u>猪八戒</u>对<u>孙悟空</u>说："我们也去摘几个人参果尝尝吧。"

<u>孙悟空</u>答应了。他跳上树，用<u>金击子</u>^{2}一敲，那人参果就掉进土^{①}里不见了。于是<u>孙悟空</u>把<u>土地神</u>叫了出来。

"是不是你偷了人参果？"<u>孙悟空</u>生气地问。

<u>土地神</u>委屈地说："不是我。人参果碰到土就会进到土里去，摘它的时候必须得用布来接。"

<u>孙悟空</u>明白了。这次，

① 土 (tǔ) *n.* soil, earth
e.g., 地上有一层土。

他等人参果掉下后，再用衣服去接。他一共敲下三个人参果，分别给了猪八戒和沙僧，又留了一个给自己。

这时候，两个徒弟正好经过他们的房间，看见他们在吃人参果，就急忙跑到院子①里去数，果然少了四个。

于是，他们就找到唐僧，生气地说："给你吃，你不吃，偏偏②要去偷！"

唐僧问自己的徒弟们："是你们摘的吗？"猪八戒不承认，沙僧也不说话。

孙悟空站出来承认："是我摘给大家吃的。"然后，他还诚恳地道歉："对不起，是我们不好，拿了你们三个人参果。我们以前没吃过，所以……"

① 院子 (yuànzi) *n.* yard
e.g., 我家后面有一个院子。

② 偏偏 (piānpiān) *adv.* willfully, insistently
e.g., 他偏偏要跟别人不一样。

① 贼 (zéi) *n.* thief
e.g., 快抓住那个贼！

② 骗子 (piànzi) *n.*
swindler, cheater
e.g., 骗子把他的钱
都骗走了。

③ 愤怒 (fènnù) *adj.*
angry, wrathful
e.g., 他愤怒地把她
推倒在地。

"你胡说。树上少了四个人参果，你怎么说只偷了三个。你不但是个贼①，而且还是个骗子②。"小徒弟生气地说。

猪八戒也跟着说："原来你自己多吃了一个啊。"

孙悟空听了非常生气，晚上等大家都睡觉了，他悄悄跑到院子里，把人参果树推倒了。然后他带着大家偷偷离开了。

镇元大仙回来后，看着被推倒的树，愤怒③极了。他追上唐僧和徒弟们，把他们抓了回来。

孙悟空说："都是我干的，跟我师父没关系，你要打就打我吧。"

晚上，孙悟空又带着大

家逃了。可是没跑多远，就又被抓了回来。

镇元大仙对孙悟空说："如果你救不活我的树，我就要打你师父。"

孙悟空连忙阻止："我救，我救，你们别打我师父。"

这一次，又是观音菩萨帮助，把人参果树救活了。事情顺利解决，唐僧和徒弟们又出发了。

[1] 人参果（rénshēnguǒ）：Ginseng Fruit
一种仙果，形状如婴儿，有四肢和五官。据说要九千至一万年才能成熟，人吃了可以长寿。A fruit shaped like an infant with arms and legs as well as the five sense organs. It's said that after growing for nine to ten thousand years, the fruit will ripen. Whoever eats it will live a long life.

[2] 金击子（jǐnjīzi）：Golden Hammer
专门用来采摘人参的宝物。A treasure used especially for gathering the ginseng fruit.

思考题：

Answer the following questions according to the story.

1. 唐僧为什么不吃人参果？

2. 人参果需要多少年才能成熟？

3. 童子为什么说孙悟空是骗子？

15. 三打白骨精

主要人物和地点：
Main Characters and Places

白骨精（Báigǔjīng）：含冤而死又不能投胎的鬼魂，擅长变化，狡猾又通晓人类的弱点。其变化的女子形象眉眼生动而妩媚多娇，是个非常著名的妖怪，在中国甚至亚洲的其他国家可以说是家喻户晓。

White Bone Demon: She is a ghost who died because of a false charge and couldn't be reincarnated. The monster is adept at transforming. She is also crafty and has a good understanding of human beings' weaknesses. When she disguises herself as a girl, she appears to be quite attractive. She is well-known not only in China but also across Asia.

离开五庄观后，大家走进了一座山。唐僧又累又饿，孙悟空就去找吃的，其他人等他回来。

这座山上住着一个妖怪，叫白骨精。她变成一个姑娘，走过来说："你们一定饿了吧。我从家带了些吃的给你们。"

这时候，孙悟空回来了。他一下看出姑娘是妖怪变的，举起金箍棒就打。

"啊！"姑娘大叫一声，倒在地上，死了。

唐僧生气地念起了紧箍咒，孙悟空疼得受不了，赶紧承认是自己的错。

唐僧对孙悟空说："你要是再打死人，我就再多念几遍。"

84

其实，白骨精根本没有死。这次，她变成一个老妇人，哭着找女儿。

八戒说："刚才打死的一定是她的女儿。"

孙悟空看出她是妖怪，一边打一边说："你居然敢再来，这次我一定要打死你！"

老妇人也倒在地上，死了。

唐僧生气极了，"你竟然又打死了人！"说完，开始念紧箍咒。

"师父，别念了……"孙悟空疼得实在受不了了。

唐僧停下来说："你要是再打死人，就不要跟着我了。"

走着走着，过来了一个老公公①，他走过来拉住唐僧说："还我老婆，还我女儿！"

孙悟空举起金箍棒，"这次我一定不能让你跑了。"

唐僧看孙悟空又要打人，赶紧念紧箍咒，疼得孙悟空扔下了金箍棒。

妖怪看孙悟空那么②难受，就站在旁边笑。这时候，孙悟空突然举起金箍棒，一棒打死了妖怪。

被打死的妖怪变成了一堆白骨③。唐僧这才相信了孙悟空。可是猪八戒却又在旁边说："他是害怕您念紧箍咒，才变出白骨骗您的。"

唐僧居然相信了猪八戒的话，把孙悟空赶走了。

① 老公公 (lǎogōnggong) *n.* old man, grandpa
e.g., 那个老公公今年七十多岁了。

② 那么 (nàme) *adv.* so
e.g., 你那里那么冷，我才不去呢。

③ 白骨 (báigǔ) *n.* white bone (of the dead)
e.g., 那个山洞里发现了几具白骨。

Answer the following questions according to the story.

1. 白骨精为什么想抓唐僧？

2. 白骨精变化了几次？分别变成了什么？

3. 唐僧为什么要赶孙悟空走？

16. 大战 ^① 黄袍怪

主要人物和地点：
Main Characters and Places

黄袍怪（Huángpáoguài）：原来是一只狼，后修炼成仙，因为与仙女相爱而被贬下人间，成为妖怪。

Yellow Robe Demon: He used to be a wolf and became an immortal after practicing asceticism. Later, however, he falls in love with a fairy maiden, and is exiled to the human world and turns into a monster.

宝象国（Bǎoxiàng Guó）：《西游记》中一个国家的名字。
Kingdom of Elephantia: A country name in the novel.

① 大战 (dà zhàn) *v.* fight a fierce battle
e.g., 今晚中国足球队大战韩国队。

① 塔 (tǎ) *n.* tower, pagoda
e.g., 这座塔真高。

② 用力 (yònglì) *v.* exert oneself physically
e.g., 你再用点儿力。

③ 砸 (zá) *v.* pound, smash
e.g., 他把玻璃砸碎了。

　　唐僧带着猪八戒和沙和尚走到了一片森林里。唐僧饿了，猪八戒去找吃的。可是过了很久，他也没回来。

　　唐僧对沙和尚说："你去找找他吧。"

　　可是沙和尚也一直不回来。过了一会儿，唐僧决定自己去找他们回来。走着走着，来到了一座塔①下。唐僧好奇地走进去，吃惊地发现里面有一个妖怪。他刚想逃，就被抓住了。

　　沙和尚和八戒回来后，发现唐僧不见了，于是赶紧到处去找。一会儿，他们就找到了那个塔。八戒举起兵器，用力②砸③门。

　　一会儿，妖怪就冲了出来，跟八戒打了起来。

这时候，塔里有一个姑娘走过来问<u>唐僧</u>："你是谁？是怎么到这里来的？"

<u>唐僧</u>回答说："我是大唐来的和尚，被妖怪抓进来的。"

姑娘听了，伤心地说："那妖怪叫<u>黄袍怪</u>。我本来是<u>宝象国</u>的公主，十三年前被<u>黄袍怪</u>抓来当妻子。我可以告诉您怎么出去。可是，请您把这信^①交给我父亲。"

在公主的帮助下，<u>唐僧</u>逃了出去，并找到了两个徒弟。他们一起来到<u>宝象国</u>，把信交给了国王。

国王看到信后，请求<u>唐僧</u>说："求您救救我的女儿吧。"

<u>猪八戒</u>自信地答应：

① 信 (xìn) n. letter
e.g., 这封信是写给你的。

① 女婿 (nǚxu) *n.*
son-in-law
e.g., 他的女婿是美国人。

"没问题。"

可是，他们根本打不过黄袍怪，沙和尚被抓，猪八戒逃跑了。

黄袍怪变成了一个小伙子，来到宝象国，对国王说："我是您的女婿①。唐僧和他的徒弟们都是妖怪，来骗您的。"

为了证明自己说的是真的，他把唐僧变成了一只老虎，告诉国王唐僧其实是老虎变成的人。国王看到老虎很害怕，就相信了黄袍怪。

猪八戒回来了，白龙马对他说："现在只有孙悟空能救师父，你快去把他找回来吧。"

八戒说："因为白骨精的事，他一定很恨我，他才不会回来呢。"

白龙马说："孙悟空要是知道师父被抓，一定会回来的。"

猪八戒没有办法，只好去找孙悟空。果然，孙悟空听说唐僧被抓后，立刻就回来了。

孙悟空趁黄袍怪不在家，救出了沙和尚和公主。然后他变成公主的样子，等黄袍怪回来。

黄袍怪刚一回来，假公主就哭了起来。

黄袍怪连忙问："老婆，你怎么了？"

假公主回答说："你几天不回来，我想你想得头也疼，心脏也疼。"

"没关系，吃了我的仙

丹就好了。"黄袍怪把仙丹
交给公主。

"哈哈！你看我是谁！"
孙悟空变回了自己的样子，
跟黄袍怪打了起来。

终于，孙悟空打败了黄
袍怪，救出了师父。

94

思考题：
Answer the following questions according to the story.

1. 唐僧被谁抓走了？

2. 是谁在塔里偷偷放走了唐僧？

3. 最后是谁救了唐僧？

17. 莲花洞遇 ① 危险

主要人物和地点：
Main Characters and Places

金角大王和银角大王（Jīnjiǎo Dàiwang hé Yínjiǎo Dàiwang）：
金角大王原来是太上老君看金炉的童子，银角大王原来是给太上老君看银炉的童子。菩萨为了试验唐僧西天取经的决心，向太上老君借来金、银角二童，变作妖怪磨砺唐僧取经的决心。

Golden Horned King and Silver Horned King: They used to be boys helping the Grand Supreme Elderly Lord look after his gold furnace and silver furnace respectively. When Guanyin Bodhisattva turned to the Grand Supreme Elderly Lord for two boys, they were turned into monsters to test Xuanzang's determination for retrieving Buddhist scriptures.

莲花洞（Liánhuā Dòng）：妖怪金角大王和银角大王住的山洞。
Lotus Flower Cave: A place where Golden Horned King and Silver Horned King live.

① 遇 (yù) v. encounter, meet
e.g., 我在路上遇到了我的中学同学。

一天，唐僧和徒弟们在路上遇到一个受伤的道士。

"救救我！"道士请求说。

唐僧对他说："你走不了，我的马就让给你骑。"

道士说："我不能骑马。"

于是，唐僧对孙悟空说："悟空，你来背他吧。"

孙悟空一眼就看出来这个道士是妖怪变的，他把道士背上，小声说："妖怪，你是不是想抓我师父啊？"

道士笑了笑，没有回答。

孙悟空故意走得很慢，想等唐僧看不见了，杀死这个妖怪。可是，背上的道士越来越沉①。他回头一看，背上背的竟然是一座山。

孙悟空大叫一声"不好"，就去追唐僧他们。可

① 沉 (chén) *adj.*
heavy
e.g., 这箱书太沉了。

96

是，<u>唐僧</u>、<u>猪八戒</u>和<u>沙和尚</u>已经被抓走了。

就在<u>孙悟空</u>不知道怎么办的时候，两个小妖怪走了过来。

<u>孙悟空</u>变成一个老道士，问："你们从哪儿来啊？"

小妖怪说："<u>莲花洞</u>。"原来，这附近有一个<u>莲花洞</u>，里边住着<u>金角大王</u>和<u>银角大王</u>。刚刚那个道士就是<u>银角大王</u>变的。

<u>孙悟空</u>又问："要去哪儿啊？"

小妖怪回答："去抓<u>孙悟空</u>。"

<u>孙悟空</u>吃惊地问："他很厉害，你们怎么抓他啊？"

妖怪说："我们有<u>红葫芦</u>[1]和<u>玉净瓶</u>[2]。我们先叫

① 遮 (zhē) *v.* cover, hide from view e.g.,太阳被云遮住了。

② 啦 (la) *part.* (used at the end of a sentence to indicate exclamation) e.g., 太好啦！

③ 这样 (zhèyàng) *pron.* such, like this e.g., 情况就是这样。

孙悟空的名字，只要他答应了，就会被装进宝贝里，一会儿就变成水了。"

孙悟空也拿出一个红葫芦，说："我这宝贝更厉害，能把天装进来。"

为了让妖怪相信，孙悟空先飞到天上，请求神仙帮忙，听到他念咒语的时候，就把天空遮①起来。

"看好啦②！"孙悟空对着小妖怪，念起咒语。果然，天就黑了。

小妖怪看红葫芦这么厉害，赶紧说："我们用两件宝贝换你的红葫芦。怎么样？"

就这样③，孙悟空骗到了妖怪的红葫芦和玉净瓶。

[1] 红葫芦（hónghúlu）：Crimson Gourd

太上老君用来装仙丹的法器，威力极大，只要叫谁的名字，那个人答应了，他就会立刻被装进红葫芦里，再贴上太上老君的符咒，不一会儿就会化成水。A container where the Grand Supreme Elderly Lord stores the elixirs. It has vast magical power. If someone answers when his name is called, he will be absorbed into the gourd. If the Grand Supreme Elderly Lord's incantation is attached to the gourd, the people inside will quickly dissolve into water.

[2] 玉净瓶（yùjìngpíng）：Amber Purifying Pot

太上老君炼丹盛水的法器，为银角大王所保管。玉净瓶的法力和红葫芦大致一样，都能将人吸入法宝中。A container used by the Grand Supreme Elderly Lord to hold water for distilling elixirs. It is kept by Silver Horned King. People can be absorbed into the pot, which is similar to the Crimson Gourd.

思考题：

Answer the following questions according to the story.

1. 是谁抓走了唐僧？

2. 他用什么办法抓了唐僧？

3. 妖怪想用来抓孙悟空的宝贝是什么？

18. 大战银角大王

红葫芦和玉净瓶被孙悟空骗走了，金角大王非常生气。

银角大王劝他："没关系，妈妈那儿不是有幌金绳[1]吗？我们用它去抓孙悟空。"

孙悟空知道以后，变成小妖怪的样子，去请妈妈。

"唐僧抓住了吗？"妈妈问。

"抓住了。可是孙悟空还没抓住，大王请您带着幌金绳，一起去抓孙悟空。"孙悟空回答。

路上，孙悟空趁妈妈不注意，杀死了她，还把幌金绳也收了起来，自己变成老妖怪的样子，来到了莲花洞。

　　假妈妈一进门，猪八戒就看出她是孙悟空变的。

　　孙悟空想跟猪八戒开个玩笑，就对金角大王说："儿子啊，我今天不想吃唐僧，就想吃猪八戒的耳朵。"

　　猪八戒听到了，赶紧喊："猴子，你竟然想吃我的耳朵？"

　　"孙悟空！"两个妖怪吃惊地叫起来。

　　"就是我！"孙悟空拿出幌金绳来绑银角大王。

　　银角大王念了一个咒语，幌金绳反而把孙悟空绑了起来。金角大王赶紧把被骗去的红葫芦和玉净瓶拿了回来。

　　孙悟空趁他们不注意，

弄断了绳子，逃出了<u>莲花</u><u>洞</u>，还偷走了红葫芦。然后他又来到<u>莲花洞</u>外大喊："我又回来了！"

　　<u>银角大王</u>刚走出<u>莲花</u><u>洞</u>，<u>孙悟空</u>就突然对他喊："<u>银角大王</u>！"

　　"啊！"<u>银角大王</u>不小心答应了一声，他立刻被收进了红葫芦里。<u>孙悟空</u>又用这个方法抓了<u>金角大王</u>。

　　"他们是我的徒弟，放了他们吧。"大家刚要离开，<u>太上老君</u>就赶来了。

　　"以后可要管^①好徒弟啊！"<u>孙悟空</u>把<u>金角大王</u>和<u>银角大王</u>放了出来。

　　<u>唐僧</u>师徒又继续朝<u>西天</u>走去。

① 管 (guǎn) v.
manage, take care of
e.g., 当妈妈的一定
要管好孩子。

[1] 幌金绳（huǎngjīnshéng）：Golden Canopy Rope
本是太上老君的一根勒袍的腰带，被菩萨放在压龙山压龙洞的九尾狐狸精那里。故事中，金角大王和银角大王的妈妈就是九尾狐狸精变的。A belt used by the Grand Supreme Elderly Lord to fasten his robe. It is kept by Nine-tail Fox in the cave of Dragon Suppressing Hill under the arrangement of Guanyin. In the story, the mother of the two monster kings is transformed from Nine-tail Fox.

思考题：
Answer the following questions according to the story.

1. 金角大王和银角大王想请谁来一起吃唐僧肉？
2. 孙悟空是怎么拿到幌金绳的？
3. 金角大王和银角大王是谁变的？

19. 收服红孩儿

主要人物和地点：
Main Characters and Places

红孩儿（Hónghái'ér）：牛魔王和铁扇公主的儿子，使用一杆八丈火尖枪，武功非凡。他在火焰山修练三百年，口里吐火，鼻子喷烟，十分了得，经常与人赤脚打斗。

Red Boy: The son of Bull Demon King and Princess Iron Fan. He is adept at fighting with a 26-meter-long fire spear. At the Flaming Mountain, he honed his skills for 300 years so that he could spit fire from his mouth and smoke from his nose. He often fights with humans in bare feet.

牛魔王（Niúmówáng）：红孩儿的爸爸，是牛变成的妖怪，武功非凡，曾是孙悟空的结拜兄弟。

Bull Demon King: Red Boy's father and once the sworn brother of Monkey King. He transforms from a bull and excels in martial arts.

火云洞（Huǒyún Dòng）：红孩儿住的地方。
Fire Cloud Cave: The place where Red Boy lives.

106

① 救命 (jiùmìng) v.
help, save one's life
e.g., 救命啊，有人掉
到河里啦！

② 远处 (yuǎnchù) n.
distant place
e.g., 我看见一个人
从远处走来。

"救命①啊……"

"是孩子的声音。"唐僧赶紧带着大家赶过去。原来是一个孩子被吊在了树上。

"救我！"孩子请求说。

"别管他，他是妖怪。"孙悟空警告大家说。

"这么小的孩子，怎么会是妖怪。快把他放下来。"唐僧不相信。

孩子被放了下来，孙悟空主动说："我来背他吧。"

孙悟空故意慢慢地在后面走。趁大家走远了，他用力把背上的孩子往地上一摔，可是孩子不见了。

"悟空！"远处②突然传来唐僧的叫声。

"不好！"孙悟空大叫。

果然，唐僧被抓走了。

为了找师父，孙悟空叫来了土地神。

"他叫红孩儿，是牛魔王的儿子，就住在火云洞里。"土地神说。

"牛魔王是我的结拜[①]兄弟，这下事情就好办了。"孙悟空高兴地说。

孙悟空和猪八戒来到火云洞，本来以为红孩儿知道孙悟空和牛魔王是结拜兄弟后会放了唐僧。可是红孩儿不但没那么做，还吐出火把孙悟空烧伤[②]了。于是，猪八戒赶紧去找观音菩萨求救，路上却被红孩儿抓进了火云洞。

"我去看看。"孙悟空变成一只蜜蜂飞进了火云洞。

"去把我爸爸请来，和

① 结拜 (jiébài) v. become sworn brothers or sisters e.g., 他们结拜为兄弟了。

② 伤 (shāng) v. hurt e.g., 你伤哪儿了？

我一起吃唐僧。"红孩儿对小妖怪说。

"我变成牛魔王，趁妖怪不注意的时候救师父。"孙悟空想。

小妖怪走到半路上就遇到了孙悟空变的牛魔王，把他请了回来。

"爸爸，您想怎么吃唐僧？"红孩儿问。

"我今天只想吃蔬菜。"牛魔王回答。

"我爸爸从来不吃蔬菜。"红孩儿觉得不对，于是就问牛魔王："您还记得我生日是哪一天吗？"

"记① 不清楚了。"牛魔王回答。

"你不是我爸爸。"红孩儿又从嘴里吐出火。

① 记 (jì) *v.* remember, memorize
e.g., 我记不住他的名字了。

孙悟空变回自己的样子，逃出了火云洞。没办法，孙悟空只好再去找观音菩萨求救。观音菩萨帮助他救回了唐僧和猪八戒，还把红孩儿带走了。

思考题：
Answer the following questions according to the story.

1. 红孩儿有什么本领？
2. 牛魔王和孙悟空是什么关系？
3. 孙悟空变成了谁来骗红孩儿？

20. 黑水河遇危险

主要人物和地点：
Main Characters and Places

河神（Héshén）：掌管河流的神。
River God: A god who controls a river.

小鼍龙（Xiǎotuólóng）：西海龙王敖闰的外甥，其父亲是泾河龙王。他父母早亡，家里兄弟九人，数他年最幼，性最孽，水下功夫十分厉害。
Alligator (Demon): The nephew of the Dragon King of the West Sea. His father is the Dragon King of Jinghe River. His parents die early. He is the youngest of nine brothers and the most treacherous with outstanding aquatic skills.

小青龙（Xiǎoqīnglóng）：西海龙王的儿子。
Cyan Dragon: The son of the Dragon King of the West Sea.

黑水河（Hēishuǐ Hé）：河名。原来是黑水河河神住的地方，后来被小鼍龙霸占。
Black River: The name of a river where Black River God used to live. In time, Alligator Demon took over the river from Black River God.

一天，唐僧师徒来到了<u>黑水河</u>边。这条河又宽又深，水也是黑的。

"师父别着急，那儿有个划船的。"<u>孙悟空</u>指着河上的小船。

"我的船太小了，只能让两个人上来。"划船的人说。

"好，那师父和<u>八戒</u>上船吧。我们飞过去。"<u>孙悟空</u>决定后说。

船到河中心的时候，突然开始刮风，船消失了。

"糟糕，划船的人是妖怪。"<u>孙悟空</u>才明白过来。这时候，<u>河神</u>突然从旁边的小水沟^①里出来了。

"这个妖怪是<u>龙王</u>的亲戚，去年来的，他不但抢了我的河，还把我赶到了小水沟里。"河神难过地说。

"我现在就去找龙王。"说完，孙悟空就走了。

他刚走到龙宫门前，就看见一个小妖怪，手里还拿着一个请帖①。悟空拦住他，把请帖抢了过来，原来那是请龙王去吃唐僧肉②的请帖。

"您怎么来啦？"龙王见到孙悟空，客气地问。

"你都想吃我师父了，我当然要来啦！"孙悟空把请帖朝龙王扔去。

龙王看了请帖后，连忙解释说："我真的不知道这件事。他是我的外甥③小鼍龙，爸妈都已经死了，我觉得他可怜，就安排他暂时住到黑水河里。可是我没想

① 请帖 (qǐngtiě) n. invitation card
e.g., 我收到了他结婚的请帖。

② 肉 (ròu) n. meat, flesh
e.g., 他从来不吃肉。

③ 外甥 (wàisheng) n. nephew
e.g., 他妹妹的儿子是他的外甥。

衡陽峪水聖河禔府

115

到，他竟然敢抓您的师父。"

"我去把他抓回来。"龙王的儿子小青龙说。

于是，小青龙帮助孙悟空抓住了小鼍龙。唐僧和八戒被救了出来，河神也重新回到了黑水河。为了表示对悟空的感谢，河神把河水分开，从中间变出了一条路，让大家过了河。

思考题：
Answer the following questions according to the story.

1. 唐僧是怎么被妖怪抓去的？

2. 黑水河原来的主人是谁？

3. 小鼍龙想请谁来吃唐僧肉？

21. 戏弄 [1] 三妖怪

主要人物和地点：
Main Characters and Places

虎力大仙（Hǔlì Dàxiān）：由老虎修炼成的妖怪。
Tiger Power Immortal: A tiger that is transformed into a demon.

鹿力大仙（Lùlì Dàxiān）：由一只白鹿修炼成的妖怪。
Elk Power Immortal: An elk that is transformed into a demon.

羊力大仙（Yánglì Dàxiān）：由一只羊修炼成的妖怪。
Antelope Power Immortal: An antelope that is transformed into a demon.

车迟国（Chēchí Guó）：唐僧和徒弟们取经路上经过的一个国家，是小说中虚构的。
Kingdom of Chechi: A fictional state that Monk Xuanzang and his disciples pass through on their way to the Western Heaven.

[1] 戏弄 (xìnòng) v. make fun of, play tricks on
e.g., 他总是喜欢戏弄同学。

一天，唐僧师徒① 来到了车迟国。他们在路上看到一群和尚在拉车。

"快点儿干活儿②！"两个道士一边打这些和尚一边骂。

孙悟空觉得很奇怪，就走过去问是怎么回事。

"二十年前发生了旱灾③，来了三个道士——虎力大仙、鹿力大仙和羊力大仙。他们跟和尚比求雨④的本领，结果道士赢了。国王就让他们当国师[1]，从此和尚就受⑤ 欺负了。"一个和尚告诉孙悟空。

孙悟空听了很生气，杀了那两个道士，把干活儿的和尚们都放了。

晚上，孙悟空就带着猪

① 师徒 (shītú) *n.* master and disciple e.g., 他们师徒俩的感情很好。

② 活儿 (huór) *n.* chores, work, job e.g., 这星期，他要在家干活儿。

③ 旱灾 (hànzāi) *n.* drought e.g., 这场旱灾给农业带来了巨大损失。

④ 求雨 (qiú yǔ) *v.* pray for rain e.g., 当地的百姓用求雨的方式，希望旱灾早点儿过去。

⑤ 受 (shòu) *v.* suffer from, be subjected to e.g., 他今天受批评了。

① 道观 (dàoguàn) *n.*
Taoist temple
e.g., 北京有几个有
名的道观。

② 神像 (shénxiàng) *n.*
god statue
e.g., 他们跪在神像
前说着什么。

③ 祷告 (dǎogào) *v.*
pray for
e.g., 他每天都向神
祷告。

④ 盯 (dīng) *v.* stare at
e.g., 别盯着我看。

八戒、沙和尚出去玩儿。他们来到了一个道观①里，看见里面有一群道士正在神像②前祷告③。

"你们看，站在前面的那三个是妖怪。"孙悟空说。

"我看不见妖怪，只看见吃的了。"猪八戒盯④着里面的食物说。

"好。"孙悟空吹了一口气，忽然刮起一阵大风，吹得道士们没有办法继续祷告，只好都离开了。

"走，我们进去。"孙悟空带着猪八戒和沙和尚走进道观。

"我们今天也来当一回神仙。"他们变成神像的样子，大口大口地吃起来。

突然，三个妖怪来了，

看见神像前的食物都被吃了，以为是神仙来了。于是都赶紧跪下来说："神仙啊，求您再送我们一些神水①吧。"

"你们平时表现很好，我们就给你们一点儿。不过，你们先出去，不许②偷看。"孙悟空假装神仙回答说。

"好，好！"三个妖怪赶紧出去等着。

八戒笑着问："我们哪儿有神水啊？"

孙悟空拿来一个瓶子，开始往里面撒尿③。猪八戒和沙僧明白了，也跟着做。

孙悟空他们撒完尿，大声说："你们进来吧。"

三个妖怪被叫了进来。

① 神水 (shénshuǐ) n. holy water
e.g., 人们传说，那条河里的水是神水。

② 许 (xǔ) v. allow, permit (usually used as negative form)
e.g., 你不许进来。

③ 撒尿 (sāniào) v. urinate
e.g., 你不可以在这儿撒尿。

他们看到瓶子里的"神水"，都开始抢着喝。

喝到一半，一个妖怪说："这味道怎么这么奇怪。"

"我们的尿① 好喝吧。"孙悟空、猪八戒都忍不住笑了出来。

妖怪们气得把瓶子摔② 在了地上，孙悟空他们笑着跑了。

① 尿 (niào) *n.* urine
e.g., 厕所的地上都是尿。

② 摔 (shuāi) *v.* throw, fling
e.g., 他把花瓶摔在了地上。

[1] 国师（guóshī）：Royal Advisor
中国历代帝王对于佛教徒中一些学德兼备的高僧所给予的称号。但后来更多的国师出自道家。A title conferred by ancient Chinese emperors to Buddhist monks who excel in learning and virtue. Later, however, more Taoist priests became royal advisors.

思考题：
Answer the following questions according to the story.

1. 车迟国的和尚为什么会被道士欺负？

2. 三个妖怪向"神仙"求了什么？

3. "神水"是什么做的？

① 昨晚 (zuówǎn) *n.*
last night
e.g., 昨晚下了一场雨。

② 王后 (wánghòu) *n.*
queen, king's wife
e.g., 他娶了一位漂亮的王后。

③ 帮 (bāng) *v.* help
e.g., 你帮我看一下屋里有人吗？

22. 车迟国比本领

三个妖怪把昨晚①的事告诉了国王，国王生气地说："这群和尚，竟然戏弄国师，把他们都杀了。"

"您先别生气。他们既然能戏弄国师，本领一定不小。为什么不让他们和国师比一下呢？"王后②对国王说。

"好，就比求雨。谁先来？"国王说。

"我先。"虎力大仙开始念咒语。果然没过多久，就开始刮风了。

孙悟空飞到天上，对神仙们说："谁也不许帮③那个妖怪。一会儿听到我喊'下雨'再下，明白了吗？"说完，孙悟空回来了。

风停了，天也晴了。孙悟空笑着问："怎么没有下雨呢？"

虎力大仙回答说："神仙不在家。"

孙悟空指着天空说："下雨。"真的开始下雨了。孙悟空他们赢了。

"我们再比一次，比坐禅①。"虎力大仙说。

这次是唐僧跟虎力大仙比。比了一会儿，鹿力大仙变成了一只臭虫②，飞进唐僧的耳朵，弄得唐僧很痒。

孙悟空发现了，就变成一只大蜈蚣③，咬了虎力大仙一口，虎力大仙疼得从台上摔了下来，输了。

"我来跟你们比。"鹿力大仙说。

① 坐禅 (zuòchán) v. sit in meditation
e.g., 那位师傅正在坐禅。

② 臭虫 (chòuchong) n. bedbug
e.g., 我最讨厌臭虫。

③ 蜈蚣 (wúgōng) n. centipede
e.g., 我妹妹很害怕蜈蚣。

① 柜子 (guìzi) *n.*
cabinet, cupboard
e.g., 东西都在柜子里。

② 桃核 (táohé) *n.*
peach stone, peach
pit
e.g., 他把桃子吃完
了, 只剩下了桃核。

这次国王先派人往柜子① 里放一件东西, 然后让他们猜。

"放好了, 猜吧。" 国王说。

<u>鹿力大仙</u>说: "是一件漂亮的衣服。"

<u>唐僧</u>说: "是一件破衣服。"

柜子打开了, 里面果然是一件破衣服。原来, <u>孙悟空</u>悄悄进了柜子里, 把衣服撕破了。

国王又派人往柜子里放了一个东西。

"好了, 猜吧。" 国王说。

<u>羊力大仙</u>说: "是一个桃。"

<u>唐僧</u>说: "是桃核②。"

打开柜子后, 里面是一

个桃核。原来这次又是孙悟空进了柜子，把桃吃了。

第三次，国王找了一个小道士，并亲自把他藏进柜子里。

虎力大仙说："是道士。"

唐僧说："是和尚。"结果，又是唐僧猜对了。原来，孙悟空悄悄进了柜子里，给小道士剪① 了头发，换了和尚的衣服。

虎力大仙生气地说："你们敢跟我比砍头② 吗？"

孙悟空笑着回答："怎么不敢？"

国王叫人先把孙悟空的头砍下来，头落③ 到了地上，被鹿力大仙偷走了。

孙悟空用肚子大喊："头来！"

① 剪 (jiǎn) v. cut, trim
e.g., 我要去剪头发。

② 砍头 (kǎn tóu) v. chop off the head
e.g., 砍头是一种很野蛮的行为。

③ 落 (luò) v. fall
e.g., 秋天到了，叶子都落了下来。

① 掏 (tāo) *v.* draw out, pull out
e.g., 他把钱从包里掏了出来。

② 叼 (diāo) *v.* hold in the mouth
e.g., 狗把肉叼走了。

可是，头没有回来。大家都以为他要死了，这时候孙悟空的脖子上又长出了一个头。

国王又叫人把虎力大仙的头砍下来，头落到了地上，孙悟空也把虎力大仙的头偷走了。一会儿虎力大仙就死了。

鹿力大仙说："孙悟空，你敢把心脏掏①出来吗？"

孙悟空回答："怎么不敢？"说完，就拿刀把自己的肚子切开，把心脏拿了出来，玩了一会儿又放回去了。

鹿力大仙也把肚子切开了，刚把心脏拿出来，孙悟空就变出一只鹰，把鹿力大仙的心脏叼②走了。于是，鹿力大仙也死了。

羊力大仙还要比："你敢在热油①里洗澡吗？"他还没有说完，孙悟空就跳进了油锅里，开始游起泳来。

羊力大仙也跳了进去，这时，孙悟空发现锅里的油突然变凉②了。他看了看，锅里有一条小龙，一定是它把油变凉的。孙悟空把小龙从锅里抓了出来。油变得越来越热。不一会儿，羊力大仙就死了。

孙悟空对国王说："你看。"

三个国师都变了样子，一个是没有头的老虎，一个是肚子被切开的鹿③，还有一个是刚被炸④熟⑤的羊⑥。国王看后，才明白他们都是妖

① 油 (yóu) n. oil
e.g., 这个菜里有很多油。

② 凉 (liáng) adj. cool, cold
e.g., 快吃吧，菜都凉了。

③ 鹿 (lù) n. deer
e.g., 那只鹿真漂亮。

④ 炸 (zhá) v. fry
e.g., 我妈妈从来不让我吃炸的东西。

⑤ 熟 (shú) adj. cooked, done (food)
e.g., 肉还没熟。

⑥ 羊 (yáng) n. goat
e.g., 我不爱吃羊肉。

怪，连忙感谢唐僧师徒，并且宣布放了和尚，让他们重新回到了寺庙里。

第二天早上，唐僧师徒离开了车迟国，继续向西天走去。

思考题：
Answer the following questions according to the story.

1. 当知道国师被戏弄以后，国王为什么没有杀唐僧师徒？

2. 三个妖怪都和唐僧师徒比了什么？

3. 三个妖怪分别是怎么死的？

23. 陈家庄救孩子

主要人物和地点：
Main Characters and Places

灵感大王（Línggǎn Dàiwang）：他本是观音菩萨莲花池里养大的金鱼，每日浮头听经，修炼成精。手持九瓣赤铜锤，跑到通天河为妖，抢占了老鼋的住宅。冒充神明，会呼风唤雨，要村民献童男童女为代价保风调雨顺。

The Inspired King: As a goldfish raised in a lotus pond by Guanyin, he listens to the goddess reciting Buddhist scriptures every day. Over time, he transforms into a demon because of the power of the words spoken by Guanyin. Soon after, he makes his way to the Tongtian River with a nine-petal copper hammer and seizes the old tortoise's residence. He poses as a deity and requires the villagers living nearby to sacrifice their young children to him in return for favorable weather for farming.

陈家庄（Chénjiā Zhuāng）：一个村庄的名字。
Chenjiazhuang Village: The name of a village.

通天河（Tōngtiān Hé）：河的名字，其水流较猛，从高处流下，像是一条通天的河流。
Tongtian River: The name of a torrential river that flows down from the high mountain and seems like a river leading to heaven.

一天，唐僧师徒走到通天河边。河上一条船也没有，天也黑了下来，于是他们就决定到附近的人家休息一个晚上。

吃饭的时候，主人一直在哭，唐僧关心地问："您为什么哭啊？"

"通天河里有一个灵感大王，每年都要来吃孩子。今年就要吃我的孩子们了。"主人说完，又哭了起来。

"别伤心了。我替①你的儿子去。"孙悟空说。

"太谢谢您了！可是我还有一个女儿，谁替她去呢？"主人发愁地问。

孙悟空笑着说："猪八戒做女孩子最合适了。"

猪八戒不高兴地说：

① 替 (tì) v. replace
e.g., 你替我去吧。

132

"你就愿意开我玩笑！"

于是，孙悟空变成了主人儿子的样子，猪八戒变成了女儿。然后被送到了灵感大王那里。

灵感大王还没来，猪八戒害怕地对孙悟空说："不知道妖怪先吃男孩子还是女孩子？"

孙悟空说："那就让他先吃我吧。"

一会儿，灵感大王回来了。

孙悟空主动说："先吃我吧。"

妖怪十分吃惊地想："别的孩子看见我都害怕，这个男孩子很勇敢！还是先吃女孩子吧！"于是他朝着女孩子走去。

① 金鱼 (jīnyú) n.
goldfish
e.g., 他买了两条金鱼。

猪八戒赶紧说:"你还是先吃他吧。"

灵感大王不听,坚持要先吃女孩子。猪八戒害怕极了,赶紧变回原来的样子,跟妖怪打了起来。妖怪受伤了,变成了一条金鱼①逃跑了。

135

思考题:
Answer the following questions according to the story.

1. 主人为什么哭?

2. 孙悟空想出了什么办法救主人的孩子?

3. 灵感大王是什么变的?

24. 大战金鱼精

灵感大王逃跑后，又下了好几天大雪，船没办法过河，唐僧他们就在主人家多住了几天。

突然有一天，猪八戒高兴地跑回来对大家说："河里的水都冻成冰① 了，我们能过去啦。"

四个人马上出发，刚走到河中间，冰突然碎了。孙悟空飞到空中，其他人都掉进了河里。猪八戒、沙和尚游② 了上来，可是唐僧却被灵感大王抓走了。

孙悟空对猪八戒和沙和尚说："你们去把妖怪引③ 出来。"

猪八戒和沙和尚找到了灵感大王的水下宫殿④ ，猪

136

① 冰 (bīng) *n.* ice
e.g., 谁都冻成冰了。

② 游 (yóu) *v.* swim
e.g., 鱼都游走了。

③ 引 (yǐn) *v.* lure, attract
e.g., 你想办法把他引到这儿来。

④ 宫殿 (gōngdiàn) *n.* palace
e.g., 国王就住在这座宫殿里。

① 篮子 (lánzi) *n.* basket
e.g., 他提着一个篮子走了过来。

八戒在门外大声喊："妖怪，放了我师父！"

"你们还敢来！"灵感大王冲出来，跟他们打了起来。

猪八戒他们打不过灵感大王，于是他们假装逃跑，想把灵感大王引到岸上。

灵感大王的脑袋刚出水，孙悟空就朝他打去，吓得他又钻回了水里，再也不出来了。

孙悟空只好去找观音菩萨帮忙。观音菩萨来到通天河，把一个篮子①放进水里，然后开始念："死的离开，活的来；死的离开，活的来。"

一共念了七遍。这时候，篮子里竟然出现了一条

① 修炼 (xiūliàn) *v.*
practice asceticism
e.g., 传说，那个道
士修炼成了神仙。

② 乌龟 (wūguī) *n.*
tortoise
e.g., 水里有一只乌龟。

金鱼。原来，灵感大王是观音菩萨养的金鱼，它每天听观音菩萨讲佛经，终于修炼①成了一个妖怪。

观音菩萨把金鱼带了回去，唐僧也被孙悟空从通天河里救了出来。

孙悟空正准备找一条船过河，就看见一只老乌龟②从通天河里游了出来。

老乌龟对孙悟空说："通天河原来是我的家，后来被妖怪抢走了。为了感谢您赶走妖怪，我背你们过河。"

唐僧过河后，非常高兴，对老乌龟说："我怎么感谢您才好呢？"

老乌龟说："我什么都不要，麻烦您问一下如来佛祖，我什么时候能修炼成人身呢？”

唐僧答应了，师徒四人继续向西天走去。

思考题：
Answer the following questions according to the story.

1. 灵感大王想了什么办法对付唐僧师徒？
2. 孙悟空为什么不在水下救唐僧？
3. 谁帮助唐僧师徒过了河？

25. <u>女儿国</u>奇遇 [1]

主要人物和地点：
Main Characters and Places

女儿国（Nǚ'ér Guó）：传说中的国家，只有女人，没有男人。女人如果想怀孕，就去喝子母河的泉水。
Kingdom of Women and Girls: A legendary state where there are only women. If a woman wants to get pregnant, she drinks water from the Zimu (Child-Mother) River.

落胎泉（Luòtāi Quán）：落胎泉里的水可以打胎。
Luotai Spring: Water from Luotai (Abortion) Spring can be used to terminate pregnancy.

① 奇遇 (qíyù) *n.* adventure
e.g., 我对他们的奇遇很感兴趣。

唐僧他们走到了一条河边，看到河水很清，很干净。

"八戒，我有点儿渴了，你帮我去盛^①一碗水来吧。"唐僧说。

猪八戒赶紧跑到河边，给唐僧盛了一碗水。唐僧喝了半碗，剩下的半碗给了猪八戒。

休息一会儿后，大家正准备继续走。突然，唐僧和猪八戒的肚子疼了起来。

一个老人正好经过，他笑着对大家说："这里是女儿国，没有男人。女人要怀孕，就去喝那河里的水。"

"我和师父怀孕了？"猪八戒简直不敢相信。

"别着急。只要再喝点

① 盛 (chéng) v. ladle out
e.g., 你给我盛点儿米饭。

142

儿<u>落胎泉</u>里的水就没事了。"
老人说。

听完老人的话，<u>孙悟空</u>
就去了<u>落胎泉</u>，取了点儿水
带了回来。<u>唐僧</u>和<u>猪八戒</u>赶
快喝下了水。

"果然不疼了。"<u>猪八戒</u>
拍拍肚子，笑着说。

于是，大家又继续出
发了。

<u>唐僧</u>来到女儿国的<u>王
宫</u>① 里换<u>通关文牒</u>[1]。女王
一见到<u>唐僧</u>，就喜欢上了
他，想让他留下做自己的
丈夫。

"您和徒弟们先去休息
吧。"<u>女王</u>② <u>客气</u>③ 地说。

<u>唐僧</u>离开后，女王对女
官说了这件事。女官听了，
高兴地说："这可是件好事

① <u>王宫</u> (wánggōng)
n. imperial palace
e.g., 国王就住在那
座王宫里。

② <u>女王</u> (nǚwáng) *n.*
queen
e.g., 她是历史上一
位有名的女王。

③ <u>客气</u> (kèqi) *adj.*
polite, courteous
e.g., 你太客气了。

144

啊。我立刻就去跟唐僧说。"

女官来到唐僧住的地方，对他说："我们女王很喜欢您，希望您能留下做她的丈夫。"

唐僧不愿意，可是旁边的孙悟空却笑着说："您就答应吧！"

唐僧气得说不出话来。女官以为他答应了，就去向女王报告。

孙悟空解释说："我们先假装答应，把通关文牒要回来。"

女王听说唐僧答应了，赶紧把他们接到了王宫里。

要回了通关文牒，唐僧对女王说："我要去送送我的徒弟。"女王同意了。

唐僧走出王宫后，却要

跟徒弟们一起离开。女王听了，急忙拉住唐僧的胳膊不让他走。

这时候，突然刮起一阵大风，唐僧不见了。

[1] 通关文牒（tōngguān wéndié）：Ancient Chinese Passport
相当于中国古代护照，是古代通过关戍时拿的通行证。
The pass which one needed to hold when crossing borders in ancient times.

思考题：
Answer the following questions according to the story.

1. 唐僧和猪八戒为什么会怀孕？

2. 孙悟空为什么要唐僧答应跟女王结婚？

3. 唐僧和女王结婚了吗？

26. 大战蝎子精

主要人物和地点：
Main Characters and Places

蝎子精（Xiēzijīng）：由一只蝎子修炼成的女妖怪，长得貌美如花。她修行多年，武艺高强，鼻中喷火，口中吐烟，神通广大，法力无边。

Scorpion Demon: A female monster that is transformed from a scorpion. She looks beautiful and is well-versed in fighting after years of practice. She can spit fire from her nose and smoke from her mouth.

昴日星官（Mǎorì Xīngguān）：二十八星宿之一，本相是六七尺高的大公鸡，神职是"司晨啼晓"。

The Star Lord of the Pleiades: One of the 28 constellations. It appears as a 6-7 foot tall rooster with the duty of crowing at dawn.

女儿国附近住着一个蝎子精，就是她把唐僧抓走了。

"我比女王漂亮多了，您不如娶我吧。"蝎子精温柔地说。

可是，无论她怎么劝，唐僧就是不答应。

"我有很多方法能让你答应。"说完，蝎子精就抱着琵琶①，弹②了起来。

听了这音乐，唐僧就像被催眠③了似的，开始听蝎子精的话了。

"妖怪，还我师父！"这时候，孙悟空突然闯了进来。

蝎子精赶紧往外跑，孙悟空在后面一直追着她。

"让你看看我的厉害！"蝎子精突然转身，用又长又尖④的尾巴扎⑤了孙悟空

① 琵琶（pípa）
n. pipa, a Chinese stringed musical instrument with a fretted fingerboard that was historically plucked with a pick, but is now mainly plucked with the fingers
e.g., 琵琶的声音很好听。

② 弹 (tán) v. play (musical instrument like piano, guitar, etc.)
e.g., 你会弹钢琴吗？

③ 催眠 (cuīmián) v. lull sb. to sleep, hypnotize
e.g., 我想试一试催眠。

④ 尖 (jiān) adj. pointed
e.g., 猫的牙齿很尖。

⑤ 扎 (zhā) v. prick, jab
e.g., 他被针扎到了。

一下。

"好疼啊！"孙悟空疼得倒在地上。

妖怪得意地笑笑，回山洞里去了。

"你怎么啦？"猪八戒把孙悟空扶起来，"我们还是带你去女儿国看医生吧。"

"不用管我，你赶快去救师父。"孙悟空着急地说。

"好。"猪八戒拿着兵器朝蝎子精的山洞走去。

到了山洞，八戒用兵器把山洞的大门砸坏了。

蝎子精生气地冲出来："你们还敢来！"

"放了我师父，不然就打死你。"说完，八戒举起兵器打了过去。

蝎子精往八戒的嘴上吹

① 咕 (gū) *onom.*
(of a hen) cluck
e.g., 鸡在院子里咕咕地叫着。

② 公鸡 (gōngjī) *n.*
rooster
e.g., 他养了一只大公鸡。

③ 蝎子 (xiēzi) *n.*
scorpion
e.g., 我很害怕蝎子。

了一口气，八戒也疼得倒在了地上。

"咕咕咕①。"这时候，出现了一只大公鸡②，它朝着妖怪叫了几声，蝎子精立刻变成了一只蝎子③。公鸡又叫了一声，那只蝎子就死了。

原来大公鸡是昴日星官变的，他知道唐僧师徒遇到了困难，所以就来救他们了。

唐僧被救出来了，大家又继续向西天走去。

思考题：
Answer the following questions according to the story.

1. 蝎子精为什么要抓走唐僧？

2. 蝎子精用了什么办法对付孙悟空？

3. 最后谁帮助了孙悟空？

27. 三借芭蕉扇¹

主要人物和地点：
Main Characters and Places

铁扇公主（Tiěshàn Gōngzhǔ）：又叫罗刹女，得道的仙人，长得漂亮俊俏，与牛魔王结为夫妻，生有一子红孩儿。她住在翠云山芭蕉洞，拥有法宝芭蕉扇。

Princess Iron Fan: She is a beautiful immortal and is also known as Demonic Lady. She is the wife of Bull Demon King as well as the mother of Red Boy. She dwells in the Palm Leaf Cave in Mount Cuiyun and possesses the magical Palm Leaf Fan.

① 扑灭 (pūmiè) *v.*
put out (fire)
e.g., 大火终于被扑
灭了。

② 嫂子 (sǎozi) *n*
sister-in-law
e.g., 你嫂子去哪儿了?

③ 怪 (guài) *v.* blame
e.g., 你别总是怪我。

有一天，唐僧和徒弟们到了火焰山。山上烧着大火，想要去西天，必须要经过这座山。

"我们要怎么过去呢？"唐僧问。

"只有用铁扇公主的芭蕉扇，才能把火扑灭①。可是她从来不把芭蕉扇借给别人。"一位老百姓说。

"她一定会借给我的。"孙悟空自信地说。原来铁扇公主是孙悟空结拜兄弟牛魔王的妻子。

孙悟空来到铁扇公主的家，客气地说："嫂子②，把芭蕉扇借我一下。"

铁扇公主生气地说："都怪③你，观音菩萨才会把我的儿子红孩儿带走。"

"那是为了他好。你应该谢谢我。"孙悟空笑着说。

铁扇公主听完更生气了，突然用剑^①砍了孙悟空的头十几下，但孙悟空一点儿事也没有。她害怕了，刚要走，就被孙悟空拉住了。

"把芭蕉扇借给我吧。"孙悟空说。

铁扇公主举起芭蕉扇，用力一扇^②，把孙悟空扇到了五万里外的一座山上。山上住着一个神仙，他给了孙悟空一颗定风丹[2]。

孙悟空带着定风丹又去找铁扇公主。

"你竟然还来！"铁扇公主说完，又举起芭蕉扇用力扇。可是，孙悟空却一动不动。铁扇公主害怕了，跑

① 剑 (jiàn) *n.* sword
e.g., 他家里有一把剑。

② 扇 (shān) *v.* wave,
fan
e.g., 你用扇子给我扇扇风。

154

回了山洞里。

　　"把芭蕉扇借给我。"山洞里响起了<u>孙悟空</u>的声音。

　　"你在哪儿？"<u>铁扇公主</u>吃惊地问。

　　"在你肚子里。"<u>孙悟空</u>说。

　　原来，<u>孙悟空</u>趁她不注意，变成一只蜜蜂飞进了<u>铁扇公主</u>喝的茶里。

　　"快把芭蕉扇借我。"说完，<u>孙悟空</u>就在她的肚子里又踢^①又跳。

　　"我借，我借。"<u>铁扇公主</u>疼得受不了，只好答应了。

　　<u>孙悟空</u>拿着芭蕉扇来到<u>火焰山</u>。他使劲儿扇，火不但没有扑灭，反而越来越大。原来这把芭蕉扇是假的。

① 踢 (tī) *v.* kick
e.g., 他把球踢了进去。

156

孙悟空又想了个办法，他变成牛魔王的样子，从铁扇公主那里把芭蕉扇骗走了。

不久，真的牛魔王回到了家里。

铁扇公主哭着说："芭蕉扇被孙悟空骗走了。"

牛魔王听了，赶紧去追孙悟空。

孙悟空拿着芭蕉扇走着走着，突然遇到了猪八戒。

"芭蕉扇这么大，我替你拿一会儿吧。"猪八戒说。

"好啊。"孙悟空同意了。

"被骗了吧。"原来这个猪八戒是牛魔王变的。

"你！"孙悟空举起金箍棒和牛魔王打了起来。

天上的神仙正好看见

了，也来帮孙悟空。牛魔王被抓住了，孙悟空拿着芭蕉扇飞到火焰山，终于把大火扑灭了。唐僧他们高兴地上路了。

[1] 芭蕉扇（bājiāoshàn）：Palm Leaf Fan
铁扇公主的宝物，扇出的风极大，因为其属性至阴，能扇出水气，所以能灭火。Princess Iron Fan's treasure, which can create strong wind. It is *yin* (negative) in nature and can produce water vapor while fanning, so it can be used to extinguish fire.

[2] 定风丹（dìngfēngdān）：Wind Resistant Pellet
灵吉菩萨送给孙悟空的神奇药丸，孙悟空将其含在嘴里后，任由铁扇公主连着扇了几扇，仍在狂风中一动不动。A magical pellet given to Monkey King by Lingji Bodhisattva. Monkey King keeps the pellet in his mouth, which allows him to stand still against the strong wind from the Princess' waving fan.

思考题：
Answer the following questions according to the story.

1. 什么可以扑灭火焰山的大火？

2. 孙悟空用什么方法骗走了芭蕉扇？

3. 孙悟空又被谁骗了？

28. 误^① 闯<u>盘丝洞</u>

主要人物和地点:
Main Characters and Places

蜘蛛精 (Zhīzhūjīng)：由蜘蛛变成的妖怪，经常变成美女
兴妖作怪，祸害人畜。打斗激烈时会敞开怀，露出雪白的
肚子，肚脐眼丝绳乱冒。

Spider Demon: The demons which are transformed from
spiders. They often turn into beauties to hurt humans and
animals. When engaged in fierce fighting, they will expose
their white bellies so that their navels spew silk threads to
attack their rivals.

盘丝洞 (Pánsī Dòng)：蜘蛛精们住的地方，因为外围常有
蜘蛛丝缠绕，所以叫盘丝洞。

Cave of the Silken Webs: The place where the spider demons
live. Since it is cocooned in spider silk, it is called the Cave
of Silken Webs.

159

---

① 误 (wù) *v.* mistake
e.g., 我误把他看成我弟弟了。

唐僧他们走了很久，都有点儿饿了。

"前面有个房子，我去要些吃的。"唐僧对徒弟们说。

当他走近的时候，看见几个姑娘在院子里玩儿。一个姑娘看见了唐僧，对他说："请进来坐吧。"

"谢谢。"唐僧跟着姑娘们进了屋。

"您从哪儿来啊？"姑娘们问。

"我从大唐来，要去西天取佛经。"唐僧礼貌地说。

"哎呀！你就是唐僧。"一个姑娘叫了起来。

这时候，姑娘们把一碗肉递给唐僧。唐僧赶紧拒绝说："我是和尚，不吃肉。"

① 丝 (sī) *n.* silk
e.g., 这件衣服是真丝做的。

姑娘们都笑了。唐僧刚想离开，就被拦住了："既然来了，就别走了。"

"师父怎么还不回来？"徒弟们着急了。

"你们看，那个房子好奇怪啊！"八戒指着一个被白丝①包起来的房子说。

"是啊，我找土地神问问。"孙悟空叫来了土地神。

"这山上住着七个蜘蛛精，那就是她们的盘丝洞。你们的师父可能被她们抓走了。"土地神说。

就在这时候，七个姑娘从房子里走了出来，一边走一边说："我们先去洗澡，回来再吃唐僧。"

于是，孙悟空跟着她们来到了河边。

162

① 名声 (míngshēng)
n. reputation
e.g., 他的名声很好。

"我如果现在抓她们，恐怕会坏了我的名声①，"孙悟空想了想，"可是也不能让她们逃走了。"于是，他变成一只鹰，把女妖怪们的衣服都叼走了。

猪八戒看孙悟空拿了一堆衣服回来，觉得很奇怪："这是谁的衣服啊？"

孙悟空回答说："蜘蛛精的。没有了衣服，她们不敢从河里出来。现在快去救师父。"

猪八戒却说："不行，得先把妖怪打死，不然她们还会来抓师父的。"

猪八戒到了河边，妖怪们还在河里。他笑着说："天这么热，我们一起洗洗吧。"说完，就跳了下去。

妖怪们急忙出来，又吐出白丝，把<u>八戒</u>包住了。

　　<u>孙悟空</u>救出<u>唐僧</u>，又赶来救出<u>八戒</u>，并把<u>盘丝洞</u>烧了。女妖怪们害怕<u>孙悟空</u>，于是都逃跑了。

思考题：
Answer the following questions according to the story.

1.唐僧不小心进了谁的家？

2.女妖怪都是什么变的？

3.孙悟空想了什么办法对付女妖怪？

29. 黄花观遇危险

主要人物和地点：
Main Characters and Places

毗蓝婆（Pílánpó）：住在紫云山千花洞，是昴日星官的母亲，法力无边，大慈大悲。

Pilanpo Bodhisattva: Mother of the Star Lord of the Pleiades who lives in the Thousand Flowers Cave of the Ziyun (Purple Clouds) Mountain. She is omnipotent yet shows great mercy to all beings.

蜈蚣精（Wúgōngjīng）：由蜈蚣修炼成的妖怪。他身居黄花观，是个炼制丹药的道士，也是盘丝洞的七个蜘蛛精的师兄。

Centipede Demon: A monster transformed from a centipede. He lives in Huanghua Temple and is brother apprentice of the seven spider demons in the Cave of Silken Webs. He is a Taoist priest who is adept at making the elixir of life.

黄花观（Huánghuā Guàn）：道观的名字。

Huanghua Temple: Name of a Taoist temple, which literally means Yellow Flower Temple.

唐僧师徒走了两天，来到了黄花观。

"我们进去休息一下。"唐僧说。

"欢迎欢迎，师父们请喝茶。"黄花观的道士看到唐僧很高兴。

孙悟空看了看杯子里的茶，又看看道士的茶，说："为什么我们的茶和您的不一样呢？我们换换吧。"

"悟空，别闹了。"唐僧批评孙悟空，然后把茶喝光了。

"是啊，为什么要换呢？"猪八戒和沙僧也把茶喝了。

不一会儿，唐僧、猪八戒和沙僧的肚子就疼了起来。

① 害 (hài) v. harm
e.g., 这个妖怪专门
害人。

② 师妹 (shīmèi) n.
junior sister apprentice
e.g., 她是我师妹。

③ 报仇 (bàochóu) v.
revenge, avenge
e.g., 他要替你报仇。

④ 穿山甲
(chuānshānjiǎ) n.
pangolin
e.g., 他在动物园看
穿山甲。

孙悟空抓住道士，生气地问："你为什么要害①我们？"

道士笑着回答："替我师妹②报仇③。"

这时候，七个蜘蛛精过来了，原来他们是这个道士的师妹。孙悟空和他们打了起来，七个蜘蛛精不是孙悟空的对手，都被孙悟空打死了。

"让你看看我的厉害！"说完，道士脱下衣服。他的身体上竟然长着一千只眼睛，那些眼睛还放出金光，把孙悟空困住了。没有办法，孙悟空只好变成一只穿山甲④，从地下逃跑了。

"怎么办？师父、八戒和沙僧要被毒死了。"孙悟

空哭了。

这时候，一位老太太走过来告诉他：

"快去找毗蓝婆帮忙吧。"

孙悟空听了，赶紧去找毗蓝婆。毗蓝婆和孙悟空一起来到黄花观。

"妖怪，出来！"孙悟空在门外大声喊。

"你又来找死了。"道士听见孙悟空的声音，出来了。

这时候，毗蓝婆扔出一根针①，朝道士扎去。

"啊！"道士大叫一声，倒在地上，变成了一只蜈蚣。

"我这儿有三颗药，快拿去救你师父他们吧。"毗蓝婆说。

"那这只蜈蚣精呢？"

孙悟空问。

"我要把它带回去。"说完，毗蓝婆就不见了。

唐僧和八戒、沙僧吃了药，肚子就不疼了，大家就又出发了。

思考题：
Answer the following questions according to the story.

1.黄花观里的道士和蜘蛛精是什么关系？

2.那个道士的什么本领最厉害？

3.最后是谁帮助了孙悟空？

30. 比丘国抓妖怪

主要人物和地点：
Main Characters and Places

老寿星（Lǎoshòuxīng）：又称南极老人星，古代中国神话中的长寿之神。

The Star of Longevity: Also known as the Elderly Star of the South Pole. He is believed to be the god of longevity according to ancient Chinese mythology.

比丘国（Bǐqiū Guó）:《西游记》中国家的名字。
Bhikkhu State: The name of a state in the novel.

一天，唐僧师徒来到了比丘国。老百姓的门外都放着一个笼子，笼子里装的都是五六岁的男孩子。

有人告诉唐僧："国王生病了，国丈①说，要用一千一百一十一个男孩子的肝②做药，病才能好。这些孩子明天就要被杀了。"

唐僧对孙悟空说："快想想办法，救救这些孩子。"

"师父别着急。"说完，孙悟空念起咒语来。突然刮起一阵风，笼子都被吹走了。

唐僧去找国王换通关文牒，孙悟空立刻就看出国丈是妖怪。这时候，有人向国王报告："孩子都被大风吹走了。"

① 国丈 (guózhàng) *n.* king's father-in-law
e.g., 他是这个国家的国丈。

② 肝 (gān) *n.* liver
e.g., 我不喜欢吃动物的肝。

172

① 藏 (cáng) *v.* hide
e.g., 你快把东西藏好。

"啊？"国王吃惊极了。

"您不用着急，我们还有办法。"国丈悄悄对国王说。

唐僧换完通关文牒就走了，孙悟空变成一只蜜蜂悄悄飞到国王旁边。

"吃了唐僧的心脏，不但可以治病，还能长生不老。"国丈笑着说。

国王高兴地说："我现在就派人去抓唐僧。"

孙悟空听了，赶紧回去把师父藏①了起来，然后变成唐僧的样子，等着国王的人来。

假唐僧被带到国王面前，还没等国王说话，国丈抢着说："国王生病了，需要你的心脏做药。"

"好啊。我有很多心脏，

不知道您要那个呢？"假唐僧说完，就吐出很多心脏。

国王被吓坏了，连忙说："你都放回去吧，我不要了。"

"我看国丈有一个黑心脏，不如拿出来做药吧。"孙悟空变回了自己的样子，举起金箍棒就朝国丈打去。

国丈打不过孙悟空，带着女儿往外跑。孙悟空和猪八戒就在后面追。

最后，猪八戒打死了国丈的女儿，原来她是狐狸①变的。就在孙悟空要打死国丈的时候，老寿星来了，把国丈带走了，原来国丈是老寿星的鹿变的。

孙悟空回到比丘国，跟国王说明了事情的经过。国

王十分惭愧，他向大家保证，以后再也不做坏事了。孙悟空把笼子里的孩子都送回了家，师徒四人继续向西天走去。

思考题：
Answer the following questions according to the story.

1. 比丘国老百姓门外笼子里装的都是什么？

2. 国王要用什么做药？

3. 这两个妖怪都是什么变的？

31. 铲除老鼠精

主要人物和地点：
Main Characters and Places

老鼠精（Lǎoshǔjīng）：老鼠修炼成的女妖怪。
Mouse Demon: A female demon transformed from a mouse.

李天王（Lǐ Tiānwáng）：天上的一位神仙。他身穿铠甲，头戴宝冠，左手托塔，右手持三叉戟，还会使用宝剑。
Pagoda Bearing Heavenly King: A heavenly immortal who wears armor with a precious crown on his head. He often supports a pagoda with his left hand and holds a three-pronged halberd with his right hand. He also excels in swordsmanship.

一天，唐僧师徒走到了一片森林里，孙悟空对大家说："我去找吃的，你们等我回来。"

孙悟空刚走，唐僧就听到有人喊："救命啊！"

唐僧说："我们去看看。"

他们来到一棵大树下，看见一个女人被绑在了树上。

"救救我吧。"女人请求说。

"谁也不要救她，她是妖怪。"这时候，孙悟空突然回来了。

那女人哭着说："我被强盗绑在这里，已经三天没吃没喝了。"

唐僧听了，觉得她很可怜，就让猪八戒放了她，带着她一起走。

晚上，他们来到一个寺庙休息。就在他们住在寺庙的这几天，可怕的事情发生了。寺庙里每天都有和尚死去，大家都很害怕。

"一定是妖怪干的。"孙悟空说。

"那该怎么办？"唐僧着急地问。

"别着急，我有办法。"孙悟空回答。

到了晚上，孙悟空变成一个小和尚，在房间里念佛经。突然，刮起一阵风，房间的门打开了。

"小师父。"一个女人朝孙悟空走过来。她的红指甲又尖又长，十分可怕。

"果然是你！"孙悟空

① 牌位 (páiwèi) *n.*
memorial tablet
e.g., 房间里有两个牌位。

认出她就是森林里的那个女人，拿起金箍棒朝她打去，可是妖怪却不见了。

"师父！"孙悟空赶紧朝唐僧的房间跑，唐僧也不见了。

孙悟空又回到森林里，找到了女妖怪住的山洞，里面却没有人。可是桌子上的牌位①让他很吃惊，上面写着：父亲李天王。

于是，孙悟空找到李天王，生气地说："我师父被你女儿抓走了。

"我女儿才七岁，怎么会去抓你师父？"李天王回答。

这时候，李天王的儿子过来说："以前咱们抓了一只老鼠精，后来把她放了，她感激我们，就叫您爸爸，您忘记了吗？"

"是她！"李天王想起来了，赶紧跟着孙悟空去救唐僧。

老鼠精被抓了起来，唐僧也被救了出来，唐僧师徒又出发了。

思考题：
Answer the following questions according to the story.

1. 寺庙里发生了什么可怕的事？
2. 孙悟空为什么要去找李天王？
3. 老鼠精真的是李天王的女儿吗？

32. <u>灭法国</u>收徒弟

主要人物和地点：
Main Characters and Places

灭法国（Mièfǎ Guó）：唐僧取经经过的国家之一。灭法国
　　国王与"佛"有仇，为了报仇，国王许下一个罗天大愿，
　　要杀掉一万名僧人做圆满。

Miefa (Dharma Eliminating) State: A state through which
　　Monk Xuanzang passes during his journey in search of the
　　Buddhist scriptures. Because the king of this state harbors
　　hatred towards the Buddha, he vows to kill 10,000 monks to
　　achieve perfection.

钦法国（Qīnfǎ Guó）：灭法国国王后来将国名改为钦法国。

Qinfa (Dharma Respecting) State: The new name of Miefa
　　State as changed by its king.

唐僧他们走着走着，突然被一个妇女拦住了。

"你们不要再走了，前面就是灭法国，国王非常恨和尚，已经杀了好多和尚了。"

"那我们应该怎么办呢？"唐僧着急地说。

"我们换上百姓的衣服，戴上帽子，就没有人能看出我们是和尚了。"孙悟空建议。

于是，大家换了衣服，到灭法国里找了一个小旅馆①。

旅馆老板问："你们想要什么样子的房间？"

"给我们找一个又小又暗的房间。"孙悟空说。

"没有那样的房间。"老板回答。

"那个大箱子②就可

① 旅馆 (lǚguǎn) n.
hotel, inn
e.g., 这家旅馆太贵了。

② 箱子 (xiāngzi) n.
box, trunk
e.g., 那个箱子真重。

184

以。"孙悟空指着门口的大箱子。

"好吧。"老板同意了。

晚上，大家听到箱子外面有人说话："明天早上再报告国王。"

原来，一群强盗以为箱子里的是宝贝，就悄悄地把它抬走了。没走多远，国王的士兵就追上来了，吓得强盗们扔下箱子就跑了。士兵们抬着箱子，准备第二天再报告国王。

"怎么办？"唐僧着急了。

"我有办法。"孙悟空笑着说。他变成一只蜜蜂，飞出箱子，然后来到了王宫。趁着大家睡觉的时候，孙悟空把王宫里每个人的头发都剪光了。

① 报应 (bàoyìng)
n. due punishment, retribution
e.g., 这是他应得的报应。

② 改 (gǎi) *v.* correct, change
e.g., 他改过名字。

　　早上，国王和王后醒了，他们吃惊地发现自己的头发没有了。为了不被别人看见，国王和王后都戴上了帽子。当看见皇宫里的人都戴着帽子的时候，国王害怕了。

　　王后哭着说："都是你的错，非要杀和尚。"

　　国王认为这是报应①，再也不敢随便杀和尚了。

　　后来，国王不但没有杀唐僧师徒，而且还做了唐僧的徒弟。灭法国的名字也被改②成了钦法国。从此，钦法国里的和尚再也不用躲藏了。唐僧师徒又出发了。

思考题：
Answer the following questions according to the story.

1. 妇女为什么劝唐僧师徒不要进灭法国？

2. 唐僧师徒进灭法国时，打扮成了什么样子？

3. 灭法国的国王为什么不再杀和尚了？

33. 玉华国丢兵器

主要人物和地点：
Main Characters and Places

黄狮精（Huángshījīng）：由狮子修炼成的妖怪。
Tawny Lion Demon: A demon transformed from a lion.

玉华国（Yùhuá Guó）：唐僧师徒取经路上经过的一个国家。
Yuhua State: A state which Monk Xuanzang and his disciples
　　pass through on their journey looking for Buddhist
　　scriptures.

① 工匠 (gōng jiàng)
n. craftsman
e.g., 他是个很能干
的工匠。

这一天，唐僧师徒来到了玉华国。

玉华国的国王有三个儿子，他们觉得唐僧的徒弟很厉害，于是请他们做自己的师父。

猪八戒对王子们说："你们把我们的兵器拿去，按照它们的样子，给自己做兵器。"

"谢谢师父！"三个王子高兴地接过兵器，让工匠①们去做。

第二天早上，大王子找到师父们，着急地说："你们的兵器都不见了。"

"什么？！"三个人听了，又吃惊又生气。

"一定是工匠偷的。"猪八戒说。

"我们的老百姓都很老实，不会偷东西。"大王子说。

孙悟空想了想，问："玉华国附近有没有妖怪？"

王子回答："据说山上住着一个妖怪。"

"我们去看看。"孙悟空说完，就带着猪八戒和沙和尚上山了。

他们走着走着，遇到了两个小妖怪，一边走一边说："黄狮精弄来的三件兵器真厉害。"

另外一只小妖怪说："我们去买几头① 猪庆祝一下。"

"原来被黄狮精偷走了。"猪八戒生气地说。

"我有办法。"孙悟空打死了小妖怪，回到玉华国弄

190

① 头 (tóu) m.w. (used for animals like pigs, cows, etc.)
e.g., 草地上有一头牛。

① 竟敢 (jìng gǎn) *v.* dare, have the audacity
e.g., 你竟敢不来上课。

来几头猪，然后变成小妖怪的样子，让沙和尚假装成卖猪的人，一起去见黄狮精。

黄狮精不高兴地问："你怎么把卖猪的也带来了？"

孙悟空说："买猪的钱不够，他就跟着我们来取了。"

黄狮精说："去取钱给他。"

沙和尚说："我其实就想看看您的新兵器，钱我不要了。"

黄狮精犹豫了一下，可是还是答应了。

"这就是我的兵器。"黄狮精指着偷来的兵器，骄傲地说。

"你竟敢①偷我们的兵器！"孙悟空立刻拿回金箍棒，朝黄狮精打去。

黄狮精打不过孙悟空，于是逃跑了。

思考题:
Answer the following questions according to the story.

1. 孙悟空他们的兵器被谁偷走了?

2. 几个小妖怪要去买什么庆祝?

3. 孙悟空和沙和尚分别假扮成什么人?

34. 收服<u>九头狮子精</u>

主要人物和地点：
Main Characters and Places

九头狮子精（Jiǔtóu Shīzijīng）：神仙太乙天尊的坐骑——
　　九头狮子，他法力高强，并且辈分很高，其他的狮子妖怪
　　都管他叫爷爷。
Nine-headed Lion Demon: A lion with nine heads, on which the
　　Compassionate Deliverer from Suffering rides. He has great
　　power and high seniority, so the other lion demons call him
　　grandpa.

太乙天尊（Tàiyǐ Tiānzūn）：道教中的神仙，法力高强，在
　　神仙中的地位也很高。
Compassionate Deliverer from Suffering: A Taoist immortal
　　who possesses great power and enjoys high prestige among
　　immortals.

① 坐骑 (zuòjì) *n.*
beast for riding
e.g., 他的坐骑是一头狮子。

"谢谢师父们帮助我们收服妖怪。"玉华国国王高兴地说。

就在大家庆祝的时候，突然刮起一阵大风，除了孙悟空，所有人都不见了。

原来，黄狮精请了九头狮子精来帮忙。刚才就是九头狮子精把大家抓走的。

孙悟空打死了黄狮精，见九头狮子精很厉害，决定上天宫求救。

孙悟空来到天宫，问神仙们："你们知道九头狮子精吗？"

"它是太乙天尊的坐骑①。"一个神仙回答。

"谢谢啦，我现在就去找他。"说完，孙悟空就来到太乙天尊的家。

"来找我有什么事啊？"太乙天尊问。

"你的坐骑呢？"孙悟空故意问。

"就在我家里，我的徒弟替我看着呢。"太乙天尊回答。

"好，那你就带我去看看吧。"孙悟空说。

他们来到关九头狮子精的笼子前，却发现笼子里是空的。

"你连坐骑不见了都不知道，快跟我去救我师父吧。"孙悟空拉着太乙天尊就走。

太乙天尊跟着孙悟空来到九头狮子精的山洞，站在山洞外喊："九头狮子！"

九头狮子精一听到太

乙天尊的声音，就赶紧出来了。

"跟我回去！"太乙天尊说完，九头狮子精就变成了一头大狮子，让太乙天尊骑在它的背上。

"以后一定要看好你的坐骑啊。"孙悟空对太乙天尊说。

太乙天尊点点头，骑着狮子回去了。

孙悟空把唐僧他们从妖怪的家中救了出来，然后大家又出发了。

198

思考题：
Answer the following questions according to the story.

1. 黄狮精找了谁帮忙？
2. 孙悟空到天宫找谁帮忙？
3. 九头狮子精的主人是谁？

35. 收服犀牛精

主要人物和地点：
Main Characters and Places

犀牛精（Xīniújīng）：犀牛变成的三个妖怪，分别叫辟寒大王、辟暑大王和辟尘大王。辟寒大王手使一把钺斧，是妖精的首领；辟暑大王使用一杆大刀；辟尘大王使的是少见的奇挞藤。三妖怪都能飞云步雾，多种变化。

Rhinoceros Demons: Three demons transformed from rhinoceroses.They are called King of Cold Protection, King of Heat Protection, and King of Dust Protection. King of Cold Protection, as the head of the three demons, is armed with a battleaxe, while King of Heat Protection and King of Dust Protection are equipped with a broadsword and a rattan whip respectively. They can fly and take on different forms.

四木禽星（Sìmù Qínxīng）：修炼成仙的四个妖怪，分别是角木蛟、斗木獬、奎木狼和井木犴。角木蛟是与龙形象相似却没有角的神兽；斗木獬是一种外观似羊的神兽，头顶正中有独角，有短尾，尾巴像蜗牛；奎木狼原形是狼；井木犴是镇水的神兽（犴是古代传说中的一种走兽，古代常把它的形象画在牢狱的门上，据说是因为他能辨善恶且好打斗）。

Four Wood Beasts of Heavenly Constellations: Four immortals transformed from monsters by way of practice, including Wood Dragon of Horn, Wood Insect of Dipper, Wood Wolf of Legs, and Wood Dog of Wells. Wood Dragon of Horn looks similar to a dragon without horns. Wood Insect of Dipper resembles a goat with a horn in the middle of its head and a short tail that looks like a snail. Wood Wolf of Legs originates from a wolf. Wood Dog of Wells is adept at controlling floods. Its original form is a legendary beast whose image used to be painted on prison doors because it is said to be capable of telling good from evil and likes fighting.

金平府（Jīnpíng Fǔ）：天竺国中的一个地方，离西天已经比较近了。

Jinping Prefecture: A place in Tianzhu kingdom which is not far from Western Heaven.

① 街 (jiē) *n.* street
e.g., 咱们一起去逛街吧。

　　唐僧和徒弟们走到金平府，正好赶上元宵节[1]，街①上非常热闹。

　　"什么味道这么香啊？"唐僧问。

　　"是灯油，每年元宵节菩萨都会来取灯油。"一个老百姓回答。

　　突然刮起一阵风，人们一边跑一遍喊："菩萨来了，快走。"可是唐僧却坚持要留下。

　　果然，有三位菩萨出现在天空中，唐僧急忙跪下。孙悟空立刻看出菩萨是妖怪变的，赶紧去拉唐僧，可是唐僧已经不见了。

　　孙悟空打听到妖怪住的地方，赶紧带着师弟们来救师父。

① 斧子 (fǔzi) *n.* axe
e.g., 他用斧子把大树砍倒了。

② 棍子 (gùnzi) *n.* stick
e.g., 那儿有一根棍子。

"妖怪，出来！"孙悟空在山洞口喊。

三个妖怪听见声音，冲出来跟他们打了起来。一个妖怪拿着大刀，一个妖怪拿着斧子①，还有一个妖怪拿着棍子②。孙悟空打不过妖怪，只好逃跑了，猪八戒和沙和尚却被妖怪抓走了。

孙悟空只好去请玉帝帮忙，路上遇见了太白金星。

"那是什么样的妖怪啊？"太白金星问。

"好像是牛，一个拿着大刀，一个拿着斧子，还有一个拿着棍子。"孙悟空回答。

"是犀牛精。只有四木禽星能收服他们。"太白金星说。

孙悟空找到玉帝说了这件事，玉帝就命令四木禽星跟着孙悟空去抓犀牛精。

犀牛精们走出山洞，跟四木禽星打了起来，可是它们根本打不过四木禽星，很快就被抓起来了。

孙悟空冲进山洞，把师父和师弟① 救了出来。

猪八戒说："我们把妖怪的山洞也烧了吧，以免② 它们再回来害人。"

四木禽星点点头说："烧！"

烧了妖怪的山洞以后，唐僧和徒弟们又出发了。

① 师弟 (shīdì) *n.* junior male apprentice
e.g., 他是我的师弟。

② 以免 (yǐmiǎn) *conj.* lest
e.g., 我还是走吧，以免影响你。

[1] 元宵节（Yuánxiāo Jié）：Yuanxiao Festival
农历正月十五，又称为"上元节"，是中国传统节日之一，春节之后的第一个重要节日。
Also called the Lantern Festival, it is one of the traditional festivals in China and falls on the 15th day of the first lunar month. It is considered the first important festival after the Spring Festival.

思考题：

Answer the following questions according to the story.

1. 来取灯油的佛祖是真的佛祖吗？

2. 三个妖怪是什么动物变的？

3. 谁帮助孙悟空抓住了妖怪？

36. 真假公主

主要人物和地点：
Main Characters and Places

天竺国（Tiānzhú Guó）：天竺是古代中国以及其他东亚国家对当今印度和巴基斯坦等南亚国家的统称。

Tianzhu Kingdom: Once used by ancient China and other East Asian countries to refer to present-day India, Pakistan and some other South Asian countries.

① 绣球 (xiùqiú) n. ball of colorful silk strips e.g., 那个绣球真漂亮。

一天，唐僧和徒弟们来到天竺国附近的一个寺庙休息。天竺国离西天不远，大家都很高兴。

吃完饭，唐僧出来散步。忽然听到女人的哭声，就问："是谁在哭啊？"

一个老和尚回答："去年的一个晚上，一阵风把这个姑娘吹到了这里，她说自己是公主。我不知道她说的是不是真的，麻烦您去天竺国的时候问一问。"

第二天早上，唐僧带着徒弟们向天竺国走去。来到天竺国，街上都是人，好像在举办活动。

"今天公主要扔绣球①，谁拿到绣球，谁就是公主的丈夫。"一个老百姓告诉他们。

208

“那寺庙里的姑娘是谁呢？”孙悟空觉得有点儿奇怪，于是拉着师父去看扔绣球。

公主在人群里看到唐僧，故意把绣球扔给了他。然后，一群人就把唐僧带进了王宫。

“你就是公主的丈夫了。”国王对唐僧说。

“可是……”唐僧刚要拒绝，孙悟空就悄悄对他说：“师父，你先留下，我再想办法救你出去。”

唐僧只好答应了。

婚礼的时间到了，唐僧的徒弟们又被请进了王宫。

公主走了出来。孙悟空一看，公主的头上有妖气，就对假公主说：“你是什么妖怪，竟敢假装公主？"

假公主知道自己打不过孙悟空，就要往外跑，孙悟空赶紧追了过去。

就在孙悟空追上妖怪，要把她杀死的时候，嫦娥突然来了。

"她是我的玉兔¹，请不要杀她。"嫦娥对孙悟空说。

玉兔被嫦娥带走了。孙悟空向国王解释了情况，真公主终于回到了王宫。

[1] 玉兔（Yùtù）：Jade Rabbit
常年陪伴在嫦娥身边的仙兔。The rabbit that accompanies Chang'e all year round.

思考题：

Answer the following questions according to the story.

1. 寺庙里关的女人到底是谁？
2. 公主扔的绣球打中了谁？
3. 假公主是谁变的？

37．西天取佛经

主要人物和地点：
Main Characters and Places

阿难（Ānán）：如来佛祖的十大弟子之一。
Ananda: One of the Buddha's ten great disciples.

迦叶（Jiāyè）：如来佛祖的十大弟子之一。
Kasyapa: One of the Buddha's ten great disciples.

八大金刚（Bādà Jīngāng）：给佛祖护法的神。
Eight Guardian Warriors: Immortals responsible for protecting
　　Dharma for the Buddhist Patriarch.

藏经阁（Cángjīng Gé）：用来藏佛经的地方。
Sutra Storage Pavilion: The place where Buddhist scriptures are
　　stored.

唐僧和徒弟们经历了许多困难，终于到了西天。

如来佛祖对自己的两个徒弟说："阿难、迦叶，你们带唐僧去取佛经。"

到了藏经阁，大家刚要去拿佛经，就被阿难拦住了。

"别着急，先把礼物拿出来。"阿难笑着说。

"我们没有准备礼物啊！"唐僧说。

"没有礼物，就不能取佛经。"迦叶说。

"不给佛经，我们就去找如来佛祖。"孙悟空生气地说。

阿难赶紧说："别去，别去。佛经现在就给你。"

取了佛经，唐僧和徒弟

们高兴地走了。

走着走着，一只大鸟飞过来，把佛经叼走了。<u>孙悟空</u>刚要去追，大鸟又把佛经还了回来。佛经掉在地上，大家赶紧去捡。

这时候，<u>唐僧</u>吃惊地说："佛经上怎么没有字？"

原来，<u>阿难</u>、<u>迦叶</u>给他们的是假佛经。

于是，大家赶紧去找<u>如来佛祖</u>。

<u>如来佛祖</u>笑着说："这件事情我已经知道了。"

<u>如来佛祖</u>又叫<u>阿难</u>、<u>迦叶</u>带着他们去取佛经。这一次，<u>阿难</u>、<u>迦叶</u>仍然要礼物。<u>唐僧</u>只好把紫金钵盂[1]给了他们，他们才终于取到了有字的佛经。

① 难 (nàn) *n.* suffering, tribulation
e.g., 这是最后一难了。

② 另 (lìng) *pron.* another, other
e.g., 另一个才是你的。

　　八大金刚负责送他们回大唐，于是大家跟着八大金刚在天上飞。

　　有个神仙对如来佛祖说："唐僧他们取经很辛苦，一共遇到了八十难①。"

　　如来佛祖说："他们一共应该遇到八十一难，现在只有八十难，还差一难。"说完，就让另②一个神仙去追唐僧。

　　唐僧他们飞着飞着，突然八大金刚消失了，唐僧他们从天上掉了下来。

　　"师父！你没事吧！"孙悟空从地上爬起来，赶紧去看唐僧。

　　"我没事。前面有条大河，我们怎么过去呢？"唐僧担心了。

"我来背你们过河。"这时候，一只老乌龟游了过来，要背大家过河。原来这条河是<u>通天河</u>，老乌龟就是以前送他们过河的那只老乌龟。

大家高兴地骑上了老乌龟的背。到了河中心的时候，老乌龟突然问<u>唐僧</u>："我请您问<u>如来佛祖</u>的问题，您问了没有？"

<u>唐僧</u>忘记问<u>如来佛祖</u>了，脸红红地不说话。

老乌龟明白了，它很生气，就把<u>唐僧</u>他们甩下了河。

"快救佛经！"<u>唐僧</u>喊。

于是，大家赶紧去捞^①佛经。还好，佛经都被捞了上来，没有丢。<u>唐僧</u>他们

① 捞 (lāo) *v.* scoop up from a liquid, dredge up e.g., 你在水里捞什么？

217

上了岸，在太阳下把佛经晒干。这时候，唐僧正好经历了八十一难。

唐僧他们回到大唐，把取来的佛经交给了大唐的皇帝唐太宗，完成了取佛经的任务。唐太宗非常高兴，请唐僧为他讲佛经。

这个时候，八大金刚出现了，带着唐僧他们一起飞上了天。到了西天，如来佛祖让唐僧师徒四个人都做了神仙，白龙马也变回了龙。

孙悟空悄悄地对唐僧说："师父，现在我头上的金箍是不是可以摘下来了？"

唐僧微笑着说："你摸摸你的头。"

孙悟空一摸，头上的金箍消失了！他高兴得不得

了。然后，大家一起听<u>如来</u>
<u>佛祖</u>讲佛经。

这就是<u>唐僧</u>西天取佛经
的故事。

[1] 紫金钵盂（Zǐjīn Bōyú）：Golden Bowl
大唐皇帝李世民赐给唐僧化缘和喝水用的食器。A container that Emperor
Taizong of the Tang Dynasty bestowed upon Monk Xuanzang to beg for
alms and to drink from on his pilgrimage.

思考题：
Answer the following questions according to the story.

1. 阿难、迦叶为什么不给唐僧师徒佛经？

2. 四大金刚送唐僧师徒回去的时候，为什么唐僧师徒从天
上掉了下去？

3. 孙悟空成了神仙以后，头上的金箍还在吗？

1. The Birth of Monkey King

Long ago, far off the sea coast, there was a mountain named Mount Huaguo, on top of which stood a giant rock. One day, the rock suddenly cracked open and a stone monkey jumped out from inside. Right after he came out, the stone monkey could run and jump with golden rays in his eyes. He lived a happy life with the other monkeys.

On a scorching hot day, all the monkeys went to play in a stream. They walked a long distance along the stream with the hope of discovering the origin of the river. When they reached the end of the stream, they saw a waterfall flowing from a hill with a cave behind it.

Although the monkeys were curious about what was in the cave, they were a little scared by the strong current.

At this moment, a senior monkey came forward and suggested, "If anyone dares to enter the cave, we will make him our king."

Upon hearing this, the stone monkey instantly answered, "I'll go!"

He then leaped through the waterfall and walked into the cave. He found that the cave looked like a spacious room and all the items inside were made of stone, such as chairs, beds, basins, bowls and so on. In the room there was a big rock engraved with three characters meaning "Water Curtain Cave," which turned out to be the name of the cave.

After a while, the stone monkey sprang out of the waterfall. He shouted to his fellows, "What a wonderful place this is! Everything we need is inside. We won't worry about the wind or rain anymore if we live inside."

Upon hearing this, all the monkeys leaped into the waterfall to look at the magic cave. It was as lovely as the stone monkey described. They touched the things and looked here and there, jumping and yelling riotously.

From then on, the Water Curtain Cave became the monkeys' home. The stone monkey was made the king of the monkeys and named himself the Handsome Monkey King.

2. Learning Skills

One day, after living peacefully for five hundred years, Monkey King said to his fellow monkeys, "Happy as we are, we will all die sooner or later." Hence all the monkeys began to feel upset.

One senior monkey suggested, "To live forever, the only way is to find a great master to learn the magic skills of immortality." Monkey King took his advice and set out to look for the master the very next day.

A few days later, Monkey King arrived at Sanxing Cave, where an immortal called Subhuti lived. Subhuti accepted him as his disciple and gave him a new name Sun Wukong.

Seven years passed by. One day, the master asked Monkey, "What do you want to learn from me?"

Monkey answered, "I would like to learn whatever you teach me."

The master said, "Divination."

Monkey asked, "Will that help me become immortal?"

The master answered, "No."

Monkey then said, "I don't want it."

The master asked, "How about making elixirs?"

Monkey asked again, "Will that help me become immortal?"

The master answered, "No."

Monkey shook his head and said, "I don't want it, either."

The master asked furiously, "What on earth do you want to learn?" He then proceeded to beat Monkey on the head three times with a ruler and went away.

Everyone blamed Monkey for his rudeness, but he didn't think so. Instead, he became cheerful. At midnight, when the clock struck three times, Monkey went into his master's room. Actually, the three hits on his head turned out to be an instruction for him to come and learn secretly at midnight.

In addition to the magic skills of being immortal, Monkey also mastered the 72 Methods of Transformation and the Somersault Cloud. After that, he became more and more complacent and showed off his skills in public from time to time.

One day, the master said to him, "You are too provocative and expose yourself too much. That will bring trouble to me someday. You have to go now."

Monkey begged, "Please! Give me one more chance!"

The master shook his head and said, "From now on, do not tell others who your master is. Will you remember this?"

Monkey nodded and left in agony.

3. Borrowing a Weapon from the Dragon King's Palace

When Monkey King returned to Mount Huaguo, the monkeys were very happy. He displayed his skills and everyone was astonished.

Monkey King said, "It's a pity that I don't have a good weapon."

A senior monkey said, "You may as well go to the Dragon Palace to find one."

Monkey King said with delight, "That's a good idea. I will go now."

Dragon King had heard that Monkey King was very powerful and dared not refuse him. He provided many weapons for him to choose from. Monkey King raised one weapon that was 1,800 kg and said it was too light.

Dragon King asked his servants to bring another one weighing more than 3,500 kg and Monkey King felt it was still too light.

Dragon King said, "This is the heaviest weapon I have. I am afraid you have to go to another place to find a suitable one."

Monkey King sat down and said with a smile, "If you can't provide one that satisfies me, I will stay here forever."

Dragon King said, "I do have another one, and if you are strong enough to carry it, I will give it to you."

Dragon King took Monkey King to the bottom of the sea, pointed to a big pillar and said, "That's it."

Monkey King tried to carry it with all his strength, but failed. He tried several more times, but ended in failure. He said, "It's too big. It would be better if it were smaller." It seemed the pillar could understand his words and became smaller.

Monkey King asked it to become smaller again, and it did as he wished. He carried it and noticed characters were written on it: "As-you-will Gold-banded Cudgel, weighing 6,750 kg".

After acquiring such a satisfying weapon, Monkey King asked for a war robe.

Dragon King became unhappy and said, "I do not have one."

Lifting the Gold-banded Cudgel up, Monkey King said, "Are you sure you don't have one? Forgive me if I do anything reckless."

Since he was so scared, Dragon King said hurriedly, "Yes, I have one. I will have it sent to you right away."

Then, Monkey King went happily back to Mount Huaguo with his Gold-banded Cudgel and beautiful war robe. The moment he left the palace, Dragon King sent a complaint against him to Jade Emperor.

4. Causing Havoc in the Heavenly Palace

Monkey King not only caused trouble at the Dragon Palace, he also crossed out his own and the other monkeys' names from the Life-and-death Book in Yama's abode. Once their names were crossed from the book, they could never die.

Yama, along with Dragon King, went to complain to Jade Emperor, who was greatly irritated.

Planet Venus then offered his advice to the emperor, "Grant a low official post to the monkey so he won't create trouble anywhere else."

Jade Emperor offered Monkey a low post where his sole duty was to raise horses in heaven.

Monkey King became overjoyed and said to the other monkeys, "Jade Emperor has invited me to the Heavenly Palace for a high post!"

One day, he asked the other immortals, "Does my post rank high?"

Everybody replied, "No, no, your post is the lowest one."

Upon hearing this, Monkey King became so angry that he flew back to Mount Huaguo. To infuriate Jade Emperor, he created a new title for himself on purpose: "The Great Sage Equal to Heaven".

This made Jade Emperor even angrier, so he dispatched troops to capture Monkey King and bring him back to heaven; however, they were no match for the powerful Monkey King.

Planet Venus then offered another suggestion, "We may as well let him be the Great Sage Equal to Heaven because it is no more than an empty title. As long as he doesn't stir up any more chaos, that will do." Therefore, Monkey King returned to the Heavenly Palace joyfully. This time he was in charge of the Heavenly Peach Garden. It was said that whoever ate its peaches would enjoy an eternal life.

Peaches were Monkey's favorite. Whenever he felt hungry, he would pick the biggest one and eat it. It was not until one day when Queen Mother was about to hold a banquet that the fairy maidens discovered that the big peaches were nowhere to be found.

Monkey asked the fairies, "Who has been invited to the banquet?"

One fairy answered, "Almost all of the immortals have been invited."

He then asked, "Was the Great Sage Equal to Heaven among those guests?"

The fairies shook their heads, saying, "We have never heard of this name."

Monkey King said angrily, "Almost everyone got invited except me! I shall ruin your banquet!"

Just before the arrival of the immortals, he snuck his way into the banquet and feasted on the food and drinks. Intoxicated, he ran to the Grand Supreme Elderly Lord and took all of the elixirs without anyone noticing.

Aware of the troubles he had caused, Monkey King flew back to Mount Huaguo.

5. Trapped Under the Five Elements Mountain

After Jade Emperor learned about what Monkey King had done, he flew into a rage. Therefore, he sent down soldiers from heaven to catch him. However, Monkey King was so powerful that all the soldiers were defeated. Jade Emperor thus had to dispatch God Erlang.

As expected, God Erlang was also quite powerful, so both of them engaged in a fierce battle for a long time, but neither could win. Just when Monkey King was caught off guard, the Grand Supreme Elderly Lord struck him on the back with the Diamond

Bracelet and captured him.

However, there was no way to kill Monkey King. The Grand Supreme Elderly Lord suggested, "Throw him into the Eight-way Trigram Furnace to burn him to death." And it was done as he ordered.

The flame in the furnace was burning more and more brilliantly. On the 49th day, the flame reached its peak. The Grand Supreme Elderly Lord said, "It's time to open the furnace."

As soon as the furnace opened, Monkey jumped out of it! He was not dead but rather gained a pair of Fiery Eyes with Golden Pupils capable of telling the evil from the good. He lifted up the Gold-banded Cudgel and shouted, "Jade Emperor, leave the Heavenly Palace to me right away." Jade Emperor hurriedly sent his servant to invite the Buddha.

The Buddha made a bet with Monkey King, "If you can jump out of my palm, I will then make you Jade Emperor. What do you think of that?"

Monkey replied happily, "Don't regret it later." With these words, he jumped on the palm of the Buddha.

After several somersaults, Monkey saw five large pillars. He thought, "Since I can travel 108,000 *li* (54,000 km) with only one somersault, I must have reached the end of heaven supported by these pillars."

Thus, he wrote a few characters on the pillars to show where he had reached. Afterwards, he jumped back to the palm of the Buddha.

Monkey said, "I have reached the end of heaven and wrote

something on the pillars."

The Buddha shook his head and said, "That is not the end of heaven but just my fingers. Look!"

Sure enough, what Monkey had written was right on the fingers of the Buddha.

Monkey said angrily, "I don't believe it! I want to look again."

At this moment, the Buddha flipped around his palm, which turned into a towering mountain pressing Monkey King underneath it. Then the Buddha attached a talisman to the mountaintop. Monkey King was thus trapped under the Five Elements Mountain.

6. Monk Xuanzang Meets His First Disciple

The Buddha wanted his teachings to be heard, but the scriptures containing his teachings could only be taken from Western Heaven by someone with no magic powers who would have to overcome numerous hardships on his way to get them. Therefore, Guanyin Bodhisattva came to Tang Dynasty China to look for the right person.

When Guanyin arrived in China, he came across a monk named Xuanzang who was preaching Buddhist scriptures. Hearing what he said, Guanyin thought he was the right person for this mission.

Thus Guanyin said to him, "In Western Heaven, there are better Buddhist scriptures. Would you like to go and get them?"

Xuanzang replied happily, "Sure, I'd love to."

Guanyin then presented to Monk Xuanzang the cassock and

cane offered by the Buddha. Xuanzang soon set forth towards Western Heaven on a white horse. Since Xuanzang was a monk of the Tang Dynasty, he was also called Monk Tang.

Monk Xuanzang arrived at the foot of a mountain and suddenly heard someone shouting, "Master, help!"

Monk Xuanzang cautiously walked over and noticed a monkey down under the mountain with only its head and hands visible. It was Monkey King who was trapped under the mountain by the Buddha nearly 500 years ago.

Upon seeing Monk Xuanzang, Monkey shouted joyfully, "Save me, Master! Guanyin Bodhisattva instructed me to be your disciple in order to escort you to obtain the Buddhist scriptures."

Xuanzang asked, "How should I save you?"

"There is a talisman on top of the mountain. Simply tear it off and that will do." Monkey pointed upwards.

Xuanzang tore it off, but Monkey went on to say, "Walk far away from here, please."

Xuanzang retreated to a faraway place immediately. Soon after, he heard a loud noise and the Five Elements Mountain collapsed. Monkey King came out and became the first disciple of Monk Xuanzang.

On their way, a flock of bandits appeared suddenly. Monkey took out his Gold-banded Cudgel and beat them all to death.

Monk Xuanzang said angrily, "How could you kill them?"

"I killed them because I need to protect you. Why do you scold me instead of thanking me! I won't go to Western Heaven anymore." With these words, Monkey King flew away.

While Monk Xuanzang was walking, he came across an old lady. She gave him a hat and said to him, "Ask your disciple to put this hat on. I will teach you a spell. Whenever he doesn't obey you, you just chant it."

This old lady was actually transformed from Guanyin Bodhisattva.

7. The White Dragon Horse

Before long, Monkey King returned. He found that Monk Xuanzang was not angry at all, but gave him a hat. Monkey put it on happily.

As soon as he put on the hat, Monk Xuanzang began to chant the Ring Tightening Mantra.

Suddenly, Monkey had a severe headache. Moaning in pain, he tried to take the hat off. Although the hat was removed, a gold ring remained on his head.

Monkey then found that it was his master who was chanting the mantra.

Monkey King begged Monk Xuanzang, "Master, please stop the mantra. I know I was wrong."

Monk Xuanzang said, "You cannot kill people at will in the future."

Monkey nodded and replied immediately, "I won't. I dare not. Please take this gold ring off my head."

Xuanzang said, "This was offered by Guanyin Bodhisattva. I cannot remove it."

Thus, Monkey King had to continue the journey with Monk Xuanzang.

One day, they came to a waterfall, where a white dragon suddenly emerged. The white dragon gulped down the horse of Monk Xuanzang in one swallow. This made Monkey so angry that he beat the white dragon with his Gold-banded Cudgel. The white dragon could not stand the fight, so he fled into the waterfall and was nowhere in sight.

Monkey King was told that the white dragon was brought there by Guanyin. Therefore, he turned to Guanyin immediately.

Guanyin said to Monkey, "The white dragon is the son of Dragon King. He committed a serious crime and would be executed. I brought him here out of mercy and intended to ask him to follow you to Western Heaven."

Monkey King replied unhappily, "Our horse has been eaten by him. How can we reach Western Heaven now?"

Guanyin replied with a smile, "Follow me and I will show you how."

Guanyin went to the waterfall and shouted, "Come out, little white dragon. Your master has arrived." Hearing this, the white dragon rushed out of the waterfall and knelt on the ground.

Guanyin cast a spell and said, "Go," the white dragon immediately turned into a beautiful white horse.

Monk Xuanzang then rode on the white horse and continued the journey to Western Heaven with Monkey King.

8. A Missing Treasure

One day, Monk Xuanzang and Monkey King went to a temple for a rest.

The senior monk who was in charge of the temple invited Monk Xuanzang to sit down and asked a young monk to serve tea.

"The tea is truly nice. Thank you," Monk Xuanzang said with a smile.

The senior monk replied, "You are flattering me. The great Tang Empire is way better than my small place. Since you come from Tang, you must have many treasures. Could you please show us some?"

Actually, the senior monk had developed a hobby of collecting a variety of treasures.

Monk Xuanzang didn't say a word. However, Monkey replied in a hurry, "Sure!" Then he showed the cassock given to his master by Guanyin.

The senior monk had never seen such a high-quality cassock before. While touching the cassock gently, he said, "What a treasure! Could you please lend me the cassock tonight and let me have a closer look?"

Monkey King agreed with eagerness, but Monk Xuanzang said to him anxiously, "It was given to me by Guanyin. If it gets lost, what shall we do then?"

Monkey replied, "Please rest assured, master. I will get the cassock back tomorrow morning."

The senior monk watched and touched it over and over again.

He liked it so much that he didn't want to return it anymore. Thus, he figured out a way to keep it.

That night, when Monk Xuanzang had fallen asleep, Monkey heard someone outside say, "Start the fire." It turned out that the senior monk decided to burn them to death.

Monkey didn't wake his master, instead he borrowed a fire proof shield from an immortal and covered the room where his master lived. The fire didn't stop spreading until the entire temple was burned up.

Behind the temple, there was a mountain where a monster named Black Wind Demon lived. When no one was looking, he snuck into the senior monk's room and stole the cassock.

With the cassock he tried so hard to obtain missing and the temple ruined, the senior monk became so grieved that he ran his head into a wall and died.

9. Smart War Against Black Wind Demon

After the death of the senior monk, Monkey asked the young monks if they had seen the cassock, but no one knew where it was. After thinking for a while, Monkey asked, "Are there any monsters nearby?"

One monk replied, "There is a monster named Black Wind Demon on the mountain out back."

"You take good care of my master and I will look for that monster right away." With that, Monkey left immediately.

Monkey went to the cave where the monster lived and shouted into the entrance, "Black Wind Demon, return my master's cassock to me at once!"

Upon hearing this, Black Wind Demon rushed out with his weapon immediately. However, he was no match to Monkey, so he quickly ran back to the cave. After that, no matter how severely Monkey cursed him, he wouldn't come out. Monkey had no other option but to turn to Guanyin for help. Guanyin agreed to offer help, so she followed Monkey to the cave.

When they were about to enter the cave, a Taoist priest came carrying a plate filled with two elixirs. Monkey discovered that the priest was transformed from a monster, so he beat him to death. After that, Guanyin turned into a priest while Monkey became an elixir.

Guanyin, disguised as a priest, entered the cave. He gave the elixir to Black Wind Demon and said, "The elixir is prepared for you. Take it, and you will live forever and never grow old ...." Before he finished his words, Black Wind Demon grabbed the elixir and swallowed it.

After entering the stomach of Black Wind Demon, Monkey began to punch and jump around inside it. Black Wind Demon could not stand the pain and begged, "It's my fault! I dare not steal your cassock anymore! Please get out of my body!"

Black Wind Demon gave the cassock back to Guanyin. Guanyin then placed a gold ring on his head.

However, as soon as Monkey came out of his stomach, Black Wind Demon wanted to kill him. At this time, Guanyin began to cast the spell. Black Wind Demon was in great pain since the gold ring on his head became tighter and tighter. He couldn't endure the pain so he had to admit his faults immediately.

After getting back the cassock, Monk Xuanzang and Monkey

left the temple and continued marching towards the west.

10. Zhu Bajie and the Gao's Village

One day, Monk Xuanzang and Monkey arrived at a place named the Gao's Village.

Several months previously, a tall and strong man, whose surname was Zhu (Pig), came to the village. The village head, Squire Gao, liked him very much, so he married his youngest daughter to him. However one day, the man turned into a monster with a pig head and a human body after he became drunk. Everyone was scared of him. Squire Gao wanted to expel him, but he insisted on staying and locked Squire Gao's daughter in a house. After hearing this, Monkey said to Squire Gao, "I assure you that I can catch the monster."

When the monster was out, Monkey saved Gao's daughter. Then, he transformed himself into Gao's daughter and waited for the monster.

After a while, the monster came back and shouted, "Sweetheart, I am back." At this moment, Monkey lifted his Gold-banded Cudgel to beat him. The monster was so scared that he ran away quickly.

Monkey recovered his normal appearance and said, "Take a look. Don't you know who I am?"

As soon as the monster found out he was Monkey King, he took out his weapon and fought with him. The monster said angrily while fighting, "You created a tremendous uproar in the Heavenly Palace in the past and now you are here to bully me." Actually, the monster used to be an immortal in heaven. However, because he flirted with the fairy Chang'e after getting drunk, Jade Emperor became very angry and turned him into a monster resembling a pig.

Since the monster was no match for Monkey, he ran away immediately. When Monkey chased after him to a cave, the monster suddenly disappeared. Monkey then broke open the entrance to the cave and rushed in.

The monster asked in fury, "Is it Squire Gao who invited you to this place?"

Monkey answered, "Guanyin ordered me to protect Monk Xuanzang on the way to acquire the Buddhist scriptures. We came across you in the Gao's Village by coincidence."

Hearing this, the monster laid down his weapon and said, "Stop fighting. I have also been dispatched by Guanyin."

From then on, the monster became the second disciple of Monk Xuanzang and was named Zhu Bajie (literally "Pig of the Eight Prohibitions") or Monk Pig.

11. Annihilating Yellow Wind Demon

One day, when Monk Xuanzang arrived at the foot of a mountain with his disciples, a strong wind suddenly blew. At this time, a tiger jumped out of the mountain and took Monk Xuanzang away.

Monkey said anxiously,"That tiger must be a demon. Hurry up! Let's go up the mountain to rescue our master."

They climbed up the mountain and discovered a cave which Monkey believed to be the demon's lair. He shouted into the cave, "Demon, release my master at once!"

At that moment, a goblin came out of the cave, but was easily killed by Monkey.

Monkey threw its body into the cave and shouted, "Demon, if you do not release my master, I will kill all of you."

In fact, it was Yellow Wind Demon who caught Monk Xuanzang, because he heard that whoever ate Monk Xuanzang could live forever.

Yellow Wind Demon was irritated by Monkey and rushed out of the cave to fight him. Monkey pulled out a body hair and transformed it into over one hundred Monkeys. Each of them struck the demon simultaneously with a Gold-banded Cudgel. Seeing this, the demon breathed out some air. The air was suddenly turned into a gale, blowing all the Monkeys down.

The demon said with a laugh, "Sun Wukong is not as powerful as I expected." With these words, he quickly returned to his cave.

Monkey transformed himself into a bee and flew into the cave, in which he found his master.

Monkey said in a low voice, "Don't be scared, Master. I'm getting you out of here."

At that time, he heard Yellow Wind Demon say to his goblins, "No one can control me except Lingji Bodhisattva."

Upon hearing this, Monkey lost no time in turning to Lingji Bodhisattva for help.

After knowing the situation, Lingji Bodhisattva took his weapon, the Flying-dragon Cane, and went to the cave with Monkey.

The goblins said to the demon without delay, "Monkey is

coming again!"

The demon answered calmly: "What are you worrying about? Wait to see how I beat him."

He came out of the cave and exhaled wind again. At this moment, the Flying-dragon Cane changed into a dragon and caught the demon with its claws. The demon vanished, but a yellow marten appeared. Actually Yellow Wind Demon was originally a yellow marten. Lingji Bodhisattva took the marten away and Monk Xuanzang and his disciples continued their journey to the west.

12. Monk Sand Joins the Team

Monk Xuanzang, together with his two disciples, continued to go west. One day, they came to the Flowing-sand River.

At the glimpse of the river, Monk Xuanzang anxiously said, "The river is so wide and deep that I may not be able to cross it."

While everyone was scratching their heads over a solution, a monster jumped out of the river and tried to catch Monk Xuanzang.

Monkey immediately protected him, while Monk Pig rushed to fight with the monster. Monkey then joined the fighting with his Gold-banded Cudgel. With the sight of Monkey, the monster jumped into the river at once.

Monk Pig said to Monkey, "I can swim and I am going to capture the monster in the river."

Monk Pig then jumped into the river and fought with the monster again. They fought into and out of the river for four hours. Monkey became impatient, so he transformed into an eagle and was ready to attack the monster. The monster saw this and quickly jumped into the water again and did not dare to pop up any more.

Without any other alternative, Monkey said to Monk Xuanzang and Monk Pig, "Master, I am going to turn to Guanyin for help. Bajie, take good care of our master."

Guanyin listened to Monkey's complaint, and said, "The monster used to be a deity in heaven. But later he did something wrong and was exiled to the Flowing-sand River to become a monster. I have persuaded him to join you in protecting Monk Xuanzang for his journey to the west. "

Then Guanyin sent a disciple to go to the Flowing-sand River together with Monkey. The disciple shouted at the river, "Come out now. Your master is here."

Hearing this, the monster jumped out of the river at once. From that point on, Monk Xuanzang had one more disciple—Monk Sand (Sandy).

In order to help the others cross the river, Monk Sand took out a precious object and changed it into a boat, bringing them safely across the river.

13. Pig Wants a Wife

"We have been walking for an entire day. I am almost starving to death! There is a house over there. Shall we take a rest there?" Pig asked.

Xuanzang nodded, so they went there together.

The house was quite big, but only a hostess and her three daughters lived there. The hostess invited them in and prepared meals for them.

While they were eating, the hostess said, "My husband died three years ago, leaving us in this house. I believe you are all good men, so you might as well stay here and marry me and my daughters."

Monk Xuanzang kept silent.

Pig said, "Look, master, how pitiful they are! Let's stay."

Monkey answered with a smile, "Bajie, you want to stay here because the daughters are beautiful and rich."

Monk Xuanzang said in anger, "You can stay if that's what you want!"

Seeing his master become angry, Pig didn't dare say more. However, after a while, he went to meet the hostess secretly, "Mother, I want to marry your daughter."

The hostess took out three garments and said, "These are my daughters' garments. You can marry the one whose garment fits you."

Pig asked with delight, "If all three fit me, can I marry all of them?"

The hostess smiled, but didn't reply.

The moment Pig held one up, the garment changed into a net, which immediately tied him up.

After the meal, Monk Xuanzang and his two other disciples went to sleep.

The next morning, Xuanzang found he was lying in the woods

and that the house they had slept in yesterday had disappeared.

It turned out that the hostess and her three daughters were transformed by Bodhisattvas to test their dedication to acquiring the Buddhist scriptures.

Just then, they heard Pig's voice up in a tree, "Help, master!"

Monkey made fun of Pig while setting him free, "You were preparing to get married, how come you ended up being hung in the tree?"

Pig blushed and said, "Master, I was wrong."

The master forgave him and continued the journey to the west with his disciples.

14. Taking Ginseng Fruit Sneakily

Immortal Zhenyuan, who lives in Wuzhuang Temple, has a ginseng fruit tree. Whoever eats the ginseng fruit would live forever. However, the fruits only ripen every 9,000 years and the tree would only bear 28 pieces of fruit. Therefore, the fruit is a rarity.

One day, Immortal Zhenyuan said to his disciples before leaving the temple, "If Monk Xuanzang comes here, pick two ginseng fruits for him."

After several days, Monk Xuanzang came to the temple as expected. The disciples picked two ginseng fruits for him as their master ordered.

Seeing the fruits, Monk Xuanzang was frightened and said, "They are but children, aren't they? How can I eat them? Take them away."

"It only looks like a child. You can eat it. Please be at ease." No matter how the disciples explained, Monk Xuanzang refused to eat the fruit.

The disciples took the fruits back and ate them themselves. What's more, they laughed at Monk Xuanzang for being so silly.

Pig said to Monkey, "Let's pick some fruits to eat."

Monkey agreed. Then he jumped onto the tree and knocked the fruit down with the Golden Hammer. The fruit fell down to the earth and disappeared. Then he summoned the God of Land.

"Is that you who stole the ginseng fruit?" Monkey asked angrily.

The God of Land replied with grievance, "Not me. The fruit will sink into the earth if it meets the soil. So you must use cloth to catch it."

Monkey understood and used a cloth to catch the fruit as it fell down. He got three pieces of fruit altogether. He gave one each to Pig, Sandy and himself.

At this time, Zhenyuan's two disciples went by their house and saw them eating the fruit. They went to count the fruit in a hurry and found that four were missing from the tree.

So they went to argue with Monk Xuanzang, "We gave them to you to eat, and you refused. Why did you steal them then?"

Monk Xuanzang asked his disciples, "Did you pick them?" Pig didn't admit it and Monk Sand kept silent.

Monkey admitted, "I picked them." He went on to apologize sincerely, "Sorry, taking the three pieces of fruit is our fault. We hadn't eaten them before, we just wanted to ...."

"Nonsense! Four fruits were missing from the tree. How can you say you only stole three? You are not only a thief, but also a liar," the younger of Zhenyuan's disciples said with anger.

Pig followed, "I see. You ate one more."

Hearing this, Monkey was annoyed. When everyone was asleep, he destroyed the tree in the yard and escaped the temple with his team secretly.

When Immortal Zhenyuan came back and saw the tree destroyed, he was greatly angered. He caught up with Monk Xuanzang and his disciples and brought them back.

Monkey said, "It is I who did all of this. It had nothing to do with my master. Beat me if you want to punish someone."

When evening arrived, Monkey managed again to run away with his team, but they were soon captured yet again.

Immortal Zhenyuan said to Monkey, "If you can't bring my tree back to life again, I will beat your master."

Monkey stopped him promptly, "I will have it revived. Please don't hurt my master."

This time, thanks to the help from Guanyin once more, the tree was brought back to life. As the problem was solved, Xuanzang continued the journey to the west with his disciples.

15. Defeating White Bone Demon

After leaving Wuzhuang Temple, they came to a mountain. Monk Xuanzang felt hungry and exhausted, so Monkey went to find food while the others waited at the site.

On this mountain there lived a monster named White Bone

Demon. She disguised herself as a girl and came towards them. "You must be hungry," she said. "I've brought something from home for you to eat."

It was at this moment that Monkey returned. He discovered that the girl was actually a monster, and thus beat her immediately with his Gold-banded Cudgel.

"Ah!!!" cried the girl before she dropped dead on the ground.

Xuanzang was furious and recited the Ring Tightening Mantra. Since Monkey could hardly endure the pain caused by the recitation, he admitted his mistake in no time.

Xuanzang warned Monkey, "If you kill someone again, I will recite the incantation more often."

In fact, White Bone Demon didn't die. She instead turned herself into an old lady, who cried along the way in search of her daughter.

Pig said, "The girl who was beaten to death just now must be her daughter."

Monkey found out she was the monster, so he said while beating her, "How dare you come back! I will kill you this time!"

The old lady dropped dead too.

Xuanzang was furious and said, "How dare you kill another!" With these words, he recited the spell again.

"Master, please stop it ...." Monkey couldn't stand the pain any more.

Xuanzang stopped and said, "If you do this a third time, you are not allowed to stay with me."

Marching on the journey, they came across an old man. The old man grabbed at Xuanzang and said to him, "Give my wife and daughter back to me."

Monkey raised his Gold-banded Cudgel and roared, "I won't let you get away again."

Realizing that Monkey was about to kill again, Xuanzang recited the spell immediately. Monkey felt so much pain that he threw his cudgel down.

While the monster was gloating over his suffering, Monkey managed to lift up his cudgel and beat him to death instantly.

The dead monster turned into a pile of white bones. Only then did Monk Xuanzang realize that Monkey was right. However, Pig said to the master, "He was frightened by your spell, so he conjured up the white bones to cheat you."

Monk Xuanzang believed Pig and chased Monkey away.

16. A Fierce Fight Against Yellow Robe Demon

When Monk Xuanzang walked into a forest with his two disciples, Pig and Sandy, he felt hungry. So he asked Pig to go and find something to eat. However, after a long period of time, Pig didn't come back.

"Go find him," Xuanzang said to Sandy.

This time, Sandy didn't return, either. Sometime later, Xuanzang decided to look for his disciples himself. He traveled on and on until he saw a pagoda. Out of curiosity, he entered it. To his surprise, he discovered a demon inside! Unfortunately, he was caught before escaping.

After their return, Sandy and Pig couldn't find their master. They hurried to look for him everywhere. Soon, they came upon the pagoda where their master had entered. Pig raised his weapon and began to pound on the door.

After some time, a monster rushed out and fought with Pig.

As this was all happening, a girl walked up to Xuanzang in the pagoda and asked, "Who are you? How did you get here?"

He answered, "I am a monk from the Tang Empire. I am being held here by the demon."

Hearing this, the girl felt sad and said, "That demon is called Yellow Robe Demon. I used to be the princess of the Kingdom of Elephantia. However, I was captured by Yellow Robe Demon and forced to marry him thirteen years ago. I can tell you the route to escape, but please deliver this letter to my father."

With the help of the princess, Xuanzang escaped and found his disciples. Together, they went to the Kingdom of Elephantia and gave the letter to the king.

The king read the letter and pleaded with Xuanzang, "Please save my daughter."

Monk Pig replied confidently, "No problem."

Unfortunately, they were no match for Yellow Robe Demon. Sandy was caught and Pig ran away.

The demon turned into a young man and came to the Kingdom of Elephantia. He said to the king, "I am your son-in-law. The monk and his disciples are monsters. They are liars."

To prove this, he changed Xuanzang into a tiger, but told the king otherwise. Since the king was so scared of the tiger, he easily believed Yellow Robe Demon.

Pig went back, and White Dragon Horse told him, "Only Monkey can save our master. Go now and ask him to come back."

Pig responded, "He must be mad at me for what I said about White Bone Demon. He won't come back."

White Dragon Horse rebutted, "If he is told that our master has been caught, he is bound to save him."

Pig had no other option than to look for Monkey. As anticipated, Monkey immediately returned when hearing of the master's imprisonment.

When the demon was not at home, Monkey rescued Sandy and the princess. He then changed into the princess and waited for the demon.

When the demon came back, the fake princess burst into tears.

"What's wrong, my dear?" the demon asked immediately.

The fake princess answered, "Since you were absent for so long, I missed you so much that my head and heart have been aching."

"Don't worry. Take the elixir and you will feel good." With these words, the demon handed the elixir to the princess.

"Haha, it's time to see who I am!" Monkey recovered his original appearance and fought the demon.

In the end, Monkey beat the demon and rescued their master.

17. Danger Around Lotus Flower Cave

One day, Monk Xuanzang and his disciples met with an injured Taoist priest on their way.

"Help me!" the priest begged.

Monk Xuanzang said to him, "You can hardly walk. Take my horse then."

The priest replied, "I can't ride a horse."

Monk Xuanzang then said to Monkey, "Wukong, please carry him on your back."

With a single glance, Monkey could see that the Taoist priest was a demon in disguise, so he hoisted the demon onto his back and whispered to him, "Demon, are you thinking of taking my master away?"

The Taoist priest smiled without saying a word.

Monkey walked slowly on purpose so that his master wouldn't see how he would kill the demon. As the demon felt heavier and heavier on his back, Monkey turned his head, only to see a hill on his back.

Monkey shouted, "No!" He immediately ran towards the direction of Xuanzang, but the three of them had already been taken away by the demon.

As Monkey was wondering what to do next, two little monsters came by.

Monkey disguised himself as a senior Taoist priest and asked, "Where do you come from?"

One little monster answered, "Lotus Flower Cave." There was a Lotus Flower Cave nearby, where Golden Horned King and Silver Horned King lived. The injured Taoist priest was actually Silver Horned King in disguise.

Monkey then asked, "Where are you heading?"

One little monster responded, "To catch Sun Wukong."

Monkey asked in astonishment, "He is omnipotent. How do you plan on catching him?"

The little monsters answered, "We have a Crimson Gourd and an Amber Purifying Pot. We will call his name—Sun Wukong—first. Once he answers, he will be inhaled in the treasures and dissolved into water quickly."

Monkey conjured up another crimson gourd and said to them, "My treasure is more powerful. It can even hold all of the heavens."

In order to convince the monsters, Monkey flew to heaven and asked the immortals for a favor. He told them to cover the sky when they heard his incantation.

"Watch closely!" Monkey said to the little monsters. Then he began to recite the incantation. As expected, the sky turned dark.

Witnessing the great power of Monkey's gourd, they asked without hesitation, "How about trading our two treasures for your gourd?"

In this way, Monkey obtained the real Crimson Gourd and the Amber Purifying Pot through his trick.

18. Fight Against Silver Horned King

Because the Crimson Gourd and Amber Purifying Pot were taken by Monkey by way of a trick, Golden Horned King became very angry.

Silver Horned King then comforted him, "Never mind. Mom has the Golden Canopy Rope and we can borrow it to catch Monkey."

When Monkey found out, he turned into a little monster and went to see their mom.

"Has Monk Xuanzang been caught?" their mom asked.

"Yes, but Monkey has escaped. The kings asked you to take the Golden Canopy Rope and catch Monkey," Monkey answered.

On the way, when the mother was preoccupied, Monkey killed her. He took away her Golden Canopy Rope and took the form of the elderly monster. Then he came to the Lotus Flower Cave.

As soon as the elderly monster stepped in, Pig recognized him.

Monkey wanted to joke with Pig, so he said to Golden Horned King, "My boy, I don't feel like eating Monk Xuanzang today. I just want to eat the pig's ears."

After hearing this, Pig immediately shouted, "Monkey, why should you eat my ears?"

"It's Monkey King!" the two monsters shouted in astonishment.

"Here I am!" Monkey took the Golden Canopy Rope out and was ready to bind Silver Horned King.

At that time, Silver Horned King recited a spell, and Monkey was tied up by the rope instead. Golden Horned King then seized this opportunity and took the Crimson Gourd and Amber Purifying Pot back.

However, Monkey secretly cut the rope and escaped from the Lotus Flower Cave with the Crimson Gourd again. He then came to the cave and yelled, "Here I am again!"

As soon as the Silver Horned King walked out of the cave, Monkey suddenly shouted his name, "Silver Horned King!"

"Ah!" the king answered unwittingly.

He was immediately absorbed in the Crimson Gourd. Monkey also caught the Golden Horned King in the same way.

"They are my disciples. Please let them go," the Grand Supreme Elderly Lord arrived as they were about to leave.

"You should discipline your disciples in the future." Then Monkey released them both.

The master and his disciples continued westward on their journey.

19. Red Boy

"Help…."

"It's the voice of a child," Monk Xuanzang said as he and his disciples hurried to find out where the cry came from. It turned out that a boy was hanging in a tree.

"Help me!" the boy pleaded.

"Leave him alone. He is a monster," Monkey warned the others.

"He is so young. How can he be a monster? Let's help him get down quickly." The master didn't believe Monkey.

The boy was untied and Monkey said, "Let me carry him!"

Monkey walked behind slowly on purpose. When the others were far ahead of him, he flung the boy to the ground powerfully. However, the boy was nowhere in sight.

"Wukong!" the master's voice rang from a distance.

"No!" Monkey called out. As expected, Monk Xuanzang was captured. In order to find his master, Monkey summoned the God of Land.

"The monster is called Red Boy, the son of Bull Demon King. He lives in the Fire Cloud Cave," the God of Land said.

"Since Bull Demon King is my sworn brother, it will be easy to rescue my master," Monkey said delightfully.

Monkey and Pig came to the Fire Cloud Cave expecting that Red Boy would release their master after learning that Monkey and Bull Demon King were sworn brothers. Instead, Red Boy spit fire to burn Monkey and injure him. Pig planned to turn to Guanyin for help, but unfortunately he was taken away into the Fire Cloud Cave by Red Boy.

"I'll go have a look." Monkey turned into a bee and flew into the Fire Cloud Cave.

"Go and invite my dad to eat Xuanzang with me," Red Boy told a little monster.

"I will turn into Bull Demon King and rescue my master when the monsters are distracted," Monkey thought.

On his way, the little monster came across the fake Bull Demon

King and invited him back.

"Dad, how do you want to eat the monk?" Red Boy asked.

"I prefer to eat vegetables today," the king answered.

"My dad never eats vegetables," Red Boy thought, beginning to doubt the king. He went on to ask, "What day is my birthday, dad?"

"I can't remember," the king answered.

"You aren't my dad!" Red Boy spit flames from his mouth again.

Monkey went back to his original appearance and escaped from the Fire Cloud Cave. He had no choice but to turn to Guanyin. Guanyin assisted him in saving his master and Pig, and took Red Boy away.

20. Facing Danger on the Black River

One day, Monk Xuanzang, along with his disciples, arrived at the bank of the Black River. The river was wide and deep with black water.

"Master, don't worry, there is a boatman over there," Monkey said as he pointed at a boat on the river.

"My boat is too small. It can only carry two of you," the boatman explained.

"Alright. Let master and Bajie take the boat while we fly over the river," Monkey made the decision.

When the boat was in the middle of the river, a sudden wind swept up and it disappeared without a trace.

"This is terrible! The boatman is a monster." Monkey realized what had happened. Just then, the River God emerged from a small ditch next to the river.

"The monster is a relative of the Dragon King. He came here last year, occupied my river and drove me into the small ditch," the River God told him in a sad tone.

"I am going to find the Dragon King." Monkey left with these words.

Approaching the Dragon Palace, he saw a little monster carrying an invitation card. Monkey stopped him and snatched away the card. It said that the Dragon King would be invited to feast on Xuanzang's flesh.

At the sight of Monkey, the Dragon King asked him politely, "What has brought you here?"

"Since you are planning to eat my master, I have to come!" Monkey threw the invitation card at the Dragon King.

Upon seeing this, the Dragon King explained at once, "I really have no idea about that. The boy is my nephew—the Alligator and his parents have died. I took pity on him and sent him to live temporarily in the Black River, but I would never have imagined he would dare to capture your master!"

"I'll go and bring him back," said Cyan Dragon, the son of the Dragon King.

With the help of Cyan Dragon, Monkey caught the Alligator Demon and rescued Xuanzang and Pig. The River God also returned to the Black River. To show his gratitude to Monkey, the River God worked out a road by parting the river so that they could cross it.

21. Playing Tricks on Three Demons

One day, Monk Xuanzang and his disciples arrived at the Kingdom of Chechi. They saw a group of monks pulling carts.

"Hurry up with your job!" two Taoist priests scolded the monks while beating them.

Monkey thought this was odd and walked towards them to find out what was going on.

"Twenty years ago, when a drought occurred, there came three Taoist priests—Tiger Power Immortal, Elk Power Immortal and Antelope Power Immortal. They competed to pray for rain with the monks and eventually the priests won. Therefore, they became the Royal Advisors, and the monks have been frequently bullied since then," one monk told Monkey.

Hearing this, Monkey became enraged. He killed the two Taoist priests and released all the monks who were working.

In the evening, Monkey took Pig and Sandy out for some fun. They arrived at a Taoist temple and saw a group of Taoist priests praying before god statues.

"Look! The three standing at the front are demons," Monkey said.

"I see no demons, only something to eat," Pig muttered, staring at the food inside.

"All right." Monkey blew a breath and a gale followed. The Taoist priests had to stop praying and leave immediately.

"Go! Let's go in." Monkey entered the temple with Pig and

Sandy.

"Let's be gods for today." They then turned themselves into god statues and began to gorge themselves on the offerings.

The three demons suddenly arrived. They found no food left in front of the god statues, and thought that the immortals had arrived. So they knelt down quickly and prayed, "Almighty Gods, would you bestow upon us more holy water?"

"Since you behave quite well at your daily service, we will offer you some. But you are not allowed to glance at us before you leave," Monkey pretended to be a god and ordered.

"Sure, sure!" the three demons went out soon and waited.

Pig giggled and then asked, "Where shall we get the holy water?"

Monkey fetched a bottle and began to urinate in it. Pig and Sandy followed suit.

After finishing, they shouted at the top of their voices, "Come in now!"

The three demons were summoned in. As soon as they saw the holy water in the bottles, they scrambled to drink it.

Drinking half a bottle, one demon asked, "Why does it taste so strange?"

"How do you like our urine?" Monkey and Pig couldn't help but laugh out loud.

The demons became so angry that they threw the bottles on the ground. Monkey and his fellows ran away with laughter.

22. Competition in the Kingdom of Chechi

After the three demons told the king what had happened the night before, the king said furiously, "How dare this gang of monks play tricks on my Royal Advisors! I'll execute all of them."

"Your Majesty, please don't be angry. Since they were able to trick your Royal Advisors, they must have some power. Why not let them compete with your Royal Advisors?" the queen suggested to the king.

"Great. Let them compete in praying for rain. Who wants to go first?" the king asked.

"I'll go first." The Tiger Power Immortal began to recite a spell. As expected, the wind soon started to blow.

Monkey flew up into the air and said to the celestial immortals, "No one is allowed to help that demon. Don't rain unless I tell you to. Understood?" With these words, Monkey returned.

The wind ceased and the sky became clear. Monkey asked with a smile, "Why isn't there any rain?"

The Tiger Power Immortal answered, "The immortals are all out today."

Monkey pointed to the sky and yelled, "Rain!" The rain really started to fall, which made him the winner.

"Let's compete in meditation," the Tiger Power Immortal suggested.

This time Monk Xuanzang would compete with him. After the competition had gone on for a long time, the Elk Power Immortal transformed himself into a bedbug. He then flew into

Xuanzang's ear and made him feel itchy.

Monkey noticed the bedbug trick, so he turned into a centipede and stung the Tiger Power Immortal. He felt so much pain that he fell off the platform and was disqualified.

"Let me compete with you," the Elk Power Immortal proposed.

This time the king first asked someone to put an object in a cabinet and then let them guess what it was.

"It's right there. You may guess now," the king said.

The Elk Power Immortal said, "It's a splendid dress."

Monk Xuanzang said, "It is a worn-out dress."

When the cabinet was opened, it turned out to be a worn-out dress. Actually, Monkey had snuck into the cabinet and torn it apart.

The king ordered another object to be put in the cabinet.

"All right. Guess again," said the king.

The Elk Power Immortal said, "It is a peach."

Xuanzang said, "It is a peach pit."

When the cabinet was opened, there was a peach pit. This time Monkey had squeezed inside to eat the peach.

During the third round, the king himself hid a young Taoist priest in the cabinet.

The Tiger Power Immortal said, "It is a Taoist priest."

Xuanzang said, "It is a monk." He made the right guess again. After entering the cabinet, Monkey had cut the priest's hair and changed his clothes into a monk's robe.

The Tiger Power Immortal exclaimed with fury, "Do you dare compete with me in chopping off the head?"

Monkey replied with a smile, "Why not?"

The king ordered that Monkey's head be cut off first. However, when his head fell down on the ground, it was stolen by the Elk Power Immortal.

Monkey shouted from his stomach, "Come here, my head!"

However, his head didn't come back. Just as everyone assumed he was going to die, another head grew on his neck.

The king then had the Tiger Power Immortal beheaded. When his head fell on the ground, Monkey stole it too. After a while, the Tiger Power Immortal died.

The Elk Power Immortal challenged, "Sun Wukong, do you have the courage to pull out your heart?"

Monkey responded, "Why not?" After saying that, he cut his own chest open with a knife, pulled out his heart, and played with it for a while before putting it back.

The Elk Power Immortal also cut his chest open. Just as he pulled out the heart, Monkey conjured up an eagle and took his heart away. As a result, the Elk Power Immortal died too.

The Antelope Power Immortal didn't give up and said, "Dare you bathe in boiling oil?" Before he finished speaking, Monkey jumped into a cauldron full of hot oil and started swimming in it.

The Antelope Power Immortal followed suit, but Monkey found

that the oil suddenly turned cold. Then he spotted a small dragon in the cauldron and suspected that it had cooled the oil down. Monkey snatched it out of the cauldron, and the oil became hotter and hotter. Soon after, the Antelope Power Immortal died.

Monkey said to the king, "Please take a look."

The Royal Advisors have all changed in appearance: a tiger without a head, a deer whose chest was sliced open, and a deep-fried sheep. Only then did the king realize they were all demons. He immediately thanked Master Xuanzang and his disciples, and announced the release of all the monks who were allowed to return to their temples.

The next morning, Master Xuanzang and his disciples left the Kingdom of Chechi and continued their journey to the west.

23. Saving Children at Chenjiazhuang Village

One day, Monk Xuanzang and his disciples reached the Tongtian River. They could see no boats on the river and the sky was getting dark, so they decided to stay overnight in a house nearby.

During dinner, the host was sobbing all the time. Xuanzang asked with great concern, "Why are you crying?"

"In the Tongtian River lives the Inspired King. He comes here every year to eat children. This year will be my children." With these words, the host began crying even more heavily.

"Don't be sad. Let me replace your son," Monkey said.

"That's very kind of you, but I also have a daughter. Who would take her place?" The host asked worryingly.

Monkey replied with a smile, "No one is more suitable than

Bajie to act as a girl."

Pig said in protest, "You are always making fun of me!"

So Monkey turned into the host's son, while Pig turned into his daughter. Both were then sent to the Inspired King.

Before the Inspired King arrived, Pig became scared and asked Monkey, "Do you think he will eat the boy or the girl first?"

Monkey replied, "Let him eat me first."

After some time, the Inspired King came.

Monkey offered, "Eat me first."

The demon was taken by surprise and thought, "Other children were all scared of seeing me. What a brave boy! I'd better eat the girl first." Then he walked towards the girl.

Pig said hastily, "Better eat him first."

The Inspired King refused to listen, and insisted on eating the girl first. Being so frightened, Pig changed himself back and fought with the demon. The demon was wounded, so he turned into a goldfish and fled.

24. A Battle with the Goldfish Demon

After the Inspired King fled, heavy snow lasted for several days and no boat could cross the river. Monk Xuanzang and his disciples had to stay a few more days at the host's house.

Then one day, Pig ran to everyone and yelled excitedly, "The river is frozen. We can cross it now."

The four set out right away. As they reached the middle of the river, the ice suddenly cracked. Monkey flew into the sky while all the others fell into the river. Pig and Sandy managed to swim to the river bank, but the master was captured by the Inspired King.

Monkey told Pig and Sandy, "You two go down to lure the monster out."

Pig and Sandy found the underwater palace of the Inspired King. Pig shouted from outside, "Monster, release our master!"

"How dare you come!" The Inspired King dashed out to fight with them.

They realized that they were no match for the monster, so they pretended to run away, hoping to lure the monster up to the river bank.

No sooner had the Inspired King lifted his head above the water than Monkey struck him. This scared the monster so greatly that it plunged into the water and never surfaced again.

Monkey could do nothing but turn to Guanyin. Guanyin came to the Tongtian River and threw a basket into it, reciting, "Go if you are dead. Come if you are alive."

After she had recited the incantation seven times, there appeared a goldfish in the basket. As a matter of fact, the Inspired King used to be a goldfish raised by Guanyin. Since it would listen to the Buddhist scriptures chanted by Guanyin every day, it had honed its skills and turned into a demon.

Guanyin took away the goldfish, and Monk Xuanzang was rescued by Monkey from the Tongtian River.

As Monkey was looking for a boat to cross the river, an old tortoise from the Tongtian River came into sight.

The old tortoise told Monkey, "This river used to be my residence but was occupied by the monster. To show appreciation for your efforts to drive away the monster, I will carry you on my back across the river."

Xuanzang felt very happy after reaching the other side of the river. He said to the old tortoise, "How can I thank you enough!"

The old tortoise replied, "I don't need any rewards. I just wonder if you can help me ask the Buddha when I will be able to transform into a human."

Xuanzang agreed. He continued the journey westward with his disciples.

25. Adventure to the Kingdom of Women and Girls

Monk Xuanzang and his disciples came to a river which was clean and translucent.

"Bajie, I feel a little thirsty. Could you help me scoop out a bowl of water from the river?" said Master Xuanzang.

Pig hurried to the riverside and scooped out a bowl of water. Xuanzang drank half and left the rest to Pig.

They rested for a while. As they were about to continue their journey, Xuanzang and Pig both began to have a stomachache.

At this time, a senior happened to pass by and said to them with a smile, "This is the Kingdom of Women and Girls, where no man lives. If a woman wants to get pregnant, she will drink the water from the river."

"Have my master and I become pregnant?" Pig could hardly believe this.

"Don't worry. You will recover if you drink some water from the Luotai Spring," said the senior.

After hearing what the senior said, Monkey went to Luotai Spring and fetched some water for them. Xuanzang and Pig drank it immediately.

"It doesn't ache anymore!" Pig said happily as he patted his belly.

Then they set off again.

Monk Xuanzang, with his disciples, arrived at the imperial palace of the Kingdom of Women and Girls to have his passport stamped. At the sight of Xuanzang, the queen immediately fell in love with him. She hoped that Xuanzang would stay and marry her.

"Please have a rest first," the queen said to them politely.

After their departure, the queen told her senior palace maid about her love for Xuanzang. The maid felt delighted and said, "That's wonderful news. I will tell Monk Xuanzang right away."

The maid came to Xuanzang's residence and told him, "Our queen loves you so much that she hopes you could stay and be her husband."

Monk Xuanzang was unwilling to do so, but Monkey said with a grin, "Just say yes!"

Xuanzang became too angry to say anything. The maid thought he agreed, so she went to report to the queen.

Monkey explained, "We will pretend to agree now so that we can get the passport."

After hearing that Monk Xuanzang agreed to marry her, the queen arranged for her maid to accommodate them in her imperial palace immediately.

Having obtained the passport, Xuanzang said to the queen, "I'd like to see my disciples off." She agreed.

Coming out of the palace, Monk Xuanzang was ready to leave with his disciples. When the queen found out about this, she clutched at Xuanzang's arm and wouldn't allow him to leave.

Just at that moment, a strong wind swept through and Monk Xuanzang was nowhere to be found.

26. The Battle Against the Scorpion Demon

Near the Kingdom of Women and Girls lived the Scorpion Demon, who captured Monk Xuanzang.

"I am far more beautiful than the queen, so you may as well marry me," the Scorpion Demon said softly.

No matter how she tried to persuade him, Monk Xuanzang wouldn't agree.

"I have many ways to make you agree with me." After saying this, she held a *pipa* and started to play it.

Having heard the music, Xuanzang seemed to be hypnotized and became obedient to her.

"Demon, release my master!" Monkey said as he broke in.

The Scorpion Demon ran away in no time and Monkey chased after her.

"Behold my power!" the Scorpion Demon turned around and

jabbed her long, pointed tail at Monkey.

"That hurts a lot!" Monkey felt so much pain that he fell to the ground.

The demon gloated over this and went back to the cave.

"What's wrong with you?" Pig assisted Monkey to his feet and said, "We'll take you to see a doctor in the Kingdom of Women and Girls."

"Don't worry about me. Go and rescue our master immediately," Monkey said anxiously.

"Okay." Pig headed to the Scorpion Demon's cave with his weapon.

Arriving at the cave, he smashed the gate with his weapon.

The Scorpion Demon rushed out angrily, "How dare you come here again!"

"Release my master, otherwise I will kill you." With these words, Pig raised his weapon to slay the demon.

At that moment, the Scorpion Demon breathed out a puff of air towards Pig's mouth. Pig ached so intensely that he collapsed on the ground.

A rooster appeared amid the sound of his own crowing. It crowed several times at the Scorpion Demon, who immediately turned into a scorpion. The rooster crowed again and the scorpion finally died.

As a matter of fact, the rooster was a transformation of the Star Lord of the Pleiades. As he was told that Monk Xuanzang and his disciples were in trouble, he came to offer them his help.

After Monk Xuanzang was saved, they continued their journey to the west.

27. Borrowing the Palm Leaf Fan

One day, Monk Xuanzang and his disciples arrived at the Flaming Mountain which had brilliant flames on it; however, in order to reach Western Heaven, they had to climb over this mountain.

"How can we cross it?" Monk Xuanzang asked.

"Only the Palm Leaf Fan from Princess Iron Fan can put out the fire, but she never lends it to others," a local resident said.

"I am sure she will lend it to me," Monkey said confidently. Actually, Princess Iron Fan was the wife of Bull Demon King, Monkey's sworn brother.

Arriving at Princess Iron Fan's home, Monkey said politely, "Sister-in-law, could you please lend me your Palm Leaf Fan?"

Princess Iron Fan furiously said, "It's your fault that Guanyin took away my son Red Boy."

"What I have done was good for him. You ought to thank me," Monkey said with a smile.

Upon hearing this, the princess became even angrier. She unexpectedly cut Monkey's head with her sword dozens of times, but he remained safe and sound. She became frightened and was about to leave when Monkey grabbed her.

"Lend me the fan, please!" Monkey said.

Princess Iron Fan raised her fan and waved it so strongly that Monkey was swept to a mountain 25,000 kilometers away. An immortal lived there who gave Monkey a wind resistant pellet.

Monkey went back to Princess Iron Fan with the pellet.

"How dare you come back again?!" After saying this, Princess Iron Fan lifted up her fan and waved it strongly again, but this time Monkey was unmoved. The princess became scared and ran back to the cave.

"Lend me the Palm Leaf Fan." Monkey's voice sounded throughout the cave.

"Where are you?" Princess Iron Fan asked in astonishment.

"In your stomach," Monkey answered.

In fact, Monkey had turned into a bee and flown into her tea without her noticing.

"Lend it to me." After saying this, Monkey began to kick and jump inside her stomach.

"I'll lend it to you. I promise!" The princess couldn't bear the pain and agreed.

Monkey took the Palm Leaf Fan to the Flaming Mountain and waved it with full strength. Unfortunately, the fire wasn't extinguished, but actually intensified. As a matter of fact, this fan was fake.

Another idea came to Monkey's mind. He decided to turn into Bull Demon King and swindle the princess out of the fan. It worked.

Soon, the real Bull Demon King returned home.

Princess Iron Fan cried, "Monkey swindled me out of the Palm

Leaf Fan."

After hearing this, Bull Demon King hurried to capture him.

While walking with the fan, Monkey bumped into Pig.

"What a huge palm leaf fan! Let me help you hold it for a while," Pig said.

"Great," Monkey agreed.

"You have been fooled!" Pig was actually Bull Demon King in disguise.

"How dare you!" Monkey raised his Gold-banded Cudgel and fought with Bull Demon King.

This happened to be seen by some celestial immortals, so they came to help Monkey King. After Bull Demon King was captured, Monkey carried the Palm Leaf Fan and flew to the Flaming Mountain. In the end, the fire was put out and Monk Xuanzang and his disciples continued their journey with delight.

28. Falling into the Cave of Silken Webs

After walking for a long time, Monk Xuanzang and his disciples felt a little hungry.

"There is a house ahead. I will look for something to eat," Xuanzang said to his disciples.

Approaching the house, he saw several girls playing in the yard. One of them noticed Monk Xuanzang and said to him, "Come in and take a seat, please."

"Thank you," Monk Xuanzang followed the girls into the house.

"Where are you from?" the girls asked.

"I am a monk from the Tang Empire. I will go to Western Heaven for the Buddhist scriptures," Monk Xuanzang answered politely.

"Alas! You are Monk Xuanzang," a girl shouted out.

At this time, the girls gave a bowl of meat to Monk Xuanzang, but he turned it down immediately, "I am a monk. I don't eat meat."

Upon hearing this, the girls burst into laughter. When Monk Xuanzang was about to leave, he was stopped, "Since you're already here, please don't go."

"Why hasn't our master returned yet?" His disciples were worried.

"Look, that house is very strange!" Pig pointed to a house cocooned in white silk.

"That's true. Let me ask the God of Land." Monkey called on him.

"There are seven spider demons on the mountain, and that house is the Cave of Silken Webs. Your master may have been caught by them," said the God of Land.

Just at that moment, the seven girls walked out of the house while talking, "Let's take a bath first and come back to eat the monk."

Monkey followed them to the riverside.

"If I catch the girls now, my reputation may suffer," Monkey thought for a while. "I can't let them run away either." So he transformed into an eagle and took the demons' clothes away.

When Pig saw Monkey bring so many clothes back, he was curious and asked, "Whose clothes are these?"

Monkey answered, "The spider demons'. Without clothes, they won't come out of the water. Let's save our master right away."

But Pig said, "No, we should kill them first, otherwise they may capture our master again."

Monk Pig went to the riverside and saw that the demons were still in the river. He shouted with a smile, "It's so hot today. Let's take a bath together." Then he jumped into the river.

The demons got out of the river immediately, spat white silk and cocooned Pig.

After rescuing their master, Monkey rushed to the scene and set Pig free. He then burned down the Cave of Silken Webs. The demons were frightened by Monkey and ran away.

29. Danger at Huanghua Temple

After two days of traveling, Monk Xuanzang, together with his disciples, arrived at Huanghua Temple.

"Let's have a rest inside," Monk Xuanzang said.

"Welcome. Please have some tea, masters," the Taoist priest there felt quite pleased to see Monk Xuanzang.

Monkey looked at the tea in his cup first, then in the priest's cup and asked, "Why does our tea look different from yours? Shall we exchange?"

"Wukong, don't be that mischievous." Having criticized Monkey, Xuanzang drank all the tea in his cup.

"Right! Why bother to swap?" Pig and Sandy also gulped the tea down.

After a while, Monk Xuanzang, Pig and Sandy all had a stomachache.

Monkey grasped the Taoist priest and asked furiously, "Why do you want to harm us?"

The Taoist priest answered with a grin, "To revenge my sister apprentices."

At this moment came the seven spider demons, who turned out to be the priest's junior sister apprentices. Monkey then engaged in a fight with them. The seven demons were no match for Monkey, so they were all killed.

"Behold my power!" With these words, the Taoist priest took off his clothes and exposed one thousand eyes on his body. All of the eyes radiated golden rays which trapped Monkey King. He had no choice but to transform into a pangolin and escape.

"What should I do? Master, Bajie and Sandy are going to be poisoned to death," Monkey cried with tears.

At that moment, an old lady came and told him, "Go and ask Pilanpo Bodhisattva for help right now."

After hearing this, Monkey hurriedly turned to Pilanpo Bodhisattva for help. She accompanied Monkey to Huanghua Temple.

"Monster, come out!" Monkey shouted outside the gate.

"You are here for death again." Hearing Monkey's voice, the priest came out.

Just at that moment, Pilanpo Bodhisattva flung a needle directly at the Taoist priest.

"Ouch!" the priest cried out, fell to the ground and turned into a centipede.

"I have three pills. Tell your master and brothers to take them quickly," Pilanpo Bodhisattva said.

"What about the Centipede Demon?" Monkey asked.

"I will take it home." After saying this, Pilanpo Bodhisattva vanished.

After taking the pills, Monk Xuanzang, Pig and Sandy recovered and they all started off again.

30. Catching the Demon in Bhikkhu State

One day, Monk Xuanzang arrived in Bhikkhu State with his disciples. There they saw a cage on each household's doorstep. In each cage was a five- or six-year-old boy.

Someone told Xuanzang, "The king's father-in-law will kill 1,111 boys tomorrow in order to use their livers to make medicine that will cure the king's disease."

Monk Xuanzang said to Monkey, "Let's quickly find a way to save these children!"

"Don't worry, master!" With these words, Monkey started to cast spells. A sudden wind came and swept all the cages away.

When Monk Xuanzang came to the king to have his passport stamped, Monkey immediately recognized that the king's father-in-law was a demon. At that time, the king was told that a heavy wind had swept away all the children.

"Ah?" the king was startled.

"Don't worry. We have other options," the king's father-in-law whispered to him.

Having had his passport stamped, Monk Xuanzang left. Monkey then turned into a bee and flew beside the king stealthily.

"If you eat Monk Xuanzang's heart, your disease can be cured, and moreover you will never grow old," the king's father-in-law said with a smile.

The king replied with delight, "I will dispatch soldiers to catch him right now."

Upon hearing this, Monkey hurried back in order to hide his master. He then transformed into his master and waited for the soldiers.

Soldiers took the fake Xuanzang to the king. Before the king spoke, his father-in-law chimed in, "We need your heart to cure the king's illness."

"No problem. I have many hearts. Which one do you want?" After saying this, the fake Xuanzang threw many hearts forward.

The king was scared at seeing this and immediately said, "I don't need any of those. Please put them back."

"I suspect your father-in-law has a black heart. Let's take it out to cure you." Monkey was restored to his original appearance and struck the King's father-in-law with his Gold-banded Cudgel.

The king's father-in-law was trounced and tried to flee with his daughter. However, Monkey and Pig chased them closely.

In the end, Pig killed the daughter, who turned out to be a fox. Before Monkey could kill the king's father-in-law, the Star of Longevity showed up and took him away. The king's father-in-law was actually a deer in disguise that belonged to the Star of Longevity.

After returning to Bhikkhu State, Monkey told the king all that had happened. The king felt very ashamed and promised that he would never do anything evil again. Monkey sent all the children who had been locked in cages back home. Monk Xuanzang, along with his disciples, continued their journey to the west.

31. Exterminating the Mouse Demon

One day, when Monk Xuanzang and his disciples walked into a forest, Monkey told the others, "I will look for something to eat. Please wait right here for me."

No sooner did Monkey leave than Xuanzang heard someone shout, "Help!"

Xuanzang said, "Let's go see what happened."

They came to a big tree and saw a woman tied to it.

"Help me, please!" the woman implored.

"Don't save her. She is a demon." Just at this time, Monkey returned unexpectedly.

"I was tied here by bandits. I've had no food or drink for three days," the woman said sadly.

Hearing this, Monk Xuanzang took pity on her, so he ordered Pig to untie her immediately and took her with them.

In the evening, they arrived at a temple for rest. During their stay, monks were dying every day, which scared everyone.

"It must be a demon," said Monkey.

"What shall we do then?" Xuanzang asked anxiously.

"Don't worry. I can solve the problem," Monkey responded.

That night, Monkey turned into a young monk and recited Buddhist scriptures in his room. Suddenly, wind blew the door open.

"Young master." Up to Monkey came a frightening woman, whose fingernails were red, long and pointed.

"Oh, here you are!" Monkey recognized that she was none other than the woman in the forest. When he was about to hit her with his Gold-banded Cudgel, the woman vanished without a trace.

"Master!" Monkey hurried to Monk Xuanzang's room, but he disappeared as well.

Monkey returned to the forest again and went to the cave where the demon lived. To his surprise, he found nobody inside except a memorial tablet on a table, which read, "Father: Pagoda Bearing Heavenly King."

Monkey then went to the Pagoda Bearing Heavenly King and furiously said, "My master was taken away by your daughter."

"How can that be possible? My daughter is only seven years old now," said the king.

Just at that time, the king's son arrived and said, "Previously, we caught a mouse demon, but let it go. Out of gratitude, she called you father. Don't you remember that?"

"It's her!" The king was reminded and followed Monkey to save Xuanzang immediately.

The Mouse Demon was captured and Monk Xuanzang was rescued. Then Xuanzang and his disciples continued on their journey.

32. A New Disciple in Miefa State

As they walked on, Master Xuanzang and his disciples were suddenly stopped by a woman.

"You'd better stop. Ahead lies Miefa State. The king there hates monks and has already killed many of them."

"What shall we do now?" Monk Xuanzang asked anxiously.

"Let's wear the clothes and hats of common people, so no one will think we're monks," Monkey suggested.

So everybody then changed their clothes and went to an inn in Miefa State.

The inn owner asked, "What type of room would you prefer?"

"We prefer a small and dark one," answered Monkey.

"No such room is available," said the owner.

"That big box will be fine," Monkey pointed to one near the doorway.

"Okay," the owner agreed.

That night, they heard someone talking outside the box, "Let's report this to the king tomorrow morning."

As a matter of fact, a group of bandits thought the box was

filled with treasure, and thus they carried it away secretly. Unfortunately for them, the king's soldiers had caught up with them not long after they left. The bandits became so frightened that they abandoned the box and ran away. The soldiers then carried the box and planned to give it to the king the next day.

"What shall we do?" Xuanzang became worried.

"I have an idea," Monkey said with a smile. Then he turned into a bee and flew out of the box to the imperial palace, where he shaved everyone's heads when they were asleep.

The next morning when the king and the queen woke up, they were surprised to find no hair on their heads. In order not to be seen by others, they put on their hats. When noticing everyone else was wearing hats, the king became scared.

The queen said in tears, "This is all your fault for killing monks."

The king thought he deserved the retribution and did not dare kill monks anymore.

Later, the king didn't kill Xuanzang or his disciples, but actually became one of Xuanzang's disciples. The name of Miefa State was then changed into Qinfa State. From then on, monks in this place no longer had to hide. Monk Xuanzang continued his journey with his disciples once again.

33. Lost Weapons in Yuhua State

One day, Master Xuanzang and his disciples arrived in Yuhua State.

The king of this state had three sons. They believed that Xuanzang's disciples were very powerful, so his sons invited them to be their masters.

Monk Pig said to the princes, "Take away our weapons, and make your own that look like ours."

"Thank you, Masters!" The princes then took the weapons with joy and asked the craftsmen to make similar ones for them.

The next morning, the eldest prince came to the masters and said anxiously, "All of your weapons are gone."

"What?!" The three masters were stunned and angry at the news.

"It must have been the craftsmen who stole them," Pig said.

"In our state, everyone is honest and wouldn't steal anything," the eldest prince said.

After thinking for a while, Monkey asked, "Are there any demons near your country?"

The prince answered, "A demon is said to live in the mountain."

"Let's go see." With these words, Monkey climbed up the mountain with Pig and Sandy.

On their way, they met two young demons who were talking with each other while walking. One demon said, "Tawny Lion Demon has acquired three really powerful weapons."

The other said, "How about buying several pigs to celebrate?"

"It is Tawny Lion Demon who stole our weapons," Pig said furiously.

"I have an idea." Monkey killed the young demons and obtained several pigs in Yuhua State. Then he transformed into a young demon and asked Sandy to act as a butcher. Then, both of them went to visit Tawny Lion Demon.

Tawny Lion Demon asked unhappily, "Why do you bring a butcher here?"

Monkey explained, "We didn't have enough money to pay for the pigs, so he came with us for the rest of it."

Tawny Lion Demon said, "Go fetch money for him then."

Sandy said, "I just want to take a look at your new weapons. I don't need the money."

Tawny Lion Demon hesitated for a moment, but agreed to his request in the end.

"These are my weapons," said Tawny Lion Demon with great pride, pointing to the stolen weapons.

"How dare you steal our weapons?" Monkey immediately snatched his Gold-banded Cudgel back and made to strike Tawny Lion Demon.

Tawny Lion Demon was no match for Monkey King, so he ran away.

34. Nine-headed Lion Demon

"Thank you so much for helping us conquer the monsters," the king of Yuhua State said cheerfully.

As everybody was celebrating, a gust suddenly blew them all away except Monkey King.

Tawny Lion Demon had turned to the Nine-headed Lion Demon for help. It was the Nine-headed Lion Demon who had seized everybody.

Monkey beat Tawny Lion Demon to death and then decided to seek help from the Heavenly Palace after seeing the power of the Nine-headed Lion Demon.

Monkey King went to the Heavenly Palace and asked the immortals, "Have you ever heard of the Nine-headed Lion Demon?"

"It is a lion on which the Compassionate Deliverer from Suffering rides," one immortal answered.

"Many thanks. I am going to look for him." With this, Monkey left for the Deliverer's residence.

"What brings you to me?" asked the Deliverer.

"Where is your lion?" Monkey King asked on purpose.

"It is kept at my house; my disciple takes care of it for me," replied the Deliverer.

"All right. Show it to me please." Monkey said.

They arrived at the cage of the Nine-headed Lion Demon, only to find an empty cage.

"You had no idea that your lion is missing. Come with me to rescue my master." Monkey pulled the immortal away and they left together immediately.

Following Monkey King, the Deliverer arrived at the cave of the Nine-headed Lion Demon. He shouted from outside, "Nine-headed Lion!"

Recognizing his voice, the demon came out right away.

"Come with me!" With these words, the demon turned into a

huge lion and the Deliverer mounted its back.

"From now on, keep a good eye on your lion," Monkey urged the immortal.

The Deliverer nodded and rode his lion home.

Monkey rescued Master Xuanzang and his fellows from the demon's house and they continued their journey.

35. Getting the Rhinoceros Demons Under Control

It happened to be the Lantern Festival when Monk Xuanzang and his disciples arrived at Jinping Prefecture, so the streets were bustling and crowded.

"What smells so good?" Monk Xuanzang asked.

"It's lamp oil. Each year the Bodhisattvas will come to fetch it," someone answered.

Suddenly, a gust of wind came and people began to run and shout, "The Bodhisattvas are coming! Let's leave soon!" However, Xuanzang insisted on staying.

As expected, three Bodhisattvas appeared in the sky, and Xuanzang knelt down at once. Nonetheless, Monkey immediately discovered that the Bodhisattvas were transformed from demons, so he hurried to grab his master. However, his master seemed to be nowhere.

After he found the demons' residence, Monkey wasted no time in rescuing his master with his fellows.

"Demons, come out!" Monkey shouted at the entrance of the cave.

Upon hearing his voice, the three demons rushed out and started to fight with them. One of the demons had a big sword, one had an axe and another had a stick. Monkey was no match for them, so he had to run away while Pig and Sandy were captured by the demons.

Monkey had to turn to Jade Emperor for help, but on his way, he encountered Planet Venus.

"What do the demons look like?" Planet Venus asked.

"They seem like bulls. One carries a sword, one has an axe, another has a stick."

"They must be Rhinoceros Demons. Only the Four Wood Beasts of Heavenly Constellations can control them," he said.

After Monkey told this to Jade Emperor, the emperor ordered the four beasts to catch the Rhinoceros Demons together with Monkey King.

As soon as the demons walked out of their cave, they started to fight with the four beasts. They were no match for the beasts, so they were captured immediately.

Monkey rushed into the cave and rescued his master and fellows.

Pig said, "Let's set fire to the cave in case the demons harm others after returning."

The beasts nodded and said, "Okay!"

Having burned down the cave, Xuanzang and his disciples continued their journey.

36. Real or Fake Princess

One day, Monk Xuanzang and his disciples arrived at a temple near Tianzhu Kingdom for a rest. Since this state was not far from Western Heaven, everyone was in high spirits.

After their meal, Xuanzang went out for a stroll. He heard a woman weeping, so he asked, "Who is crying?"

An elderly monk replied, "One night last year, a gust of wind brought a girl here. She claimed to be a princess, but we have no idea whether it is true or not. Would you mind inquiring into this when you arrive in Tianzhu?"

The next morning, Monk Xuanzang and his disciples continued their way towards Tianzhu. When arriving, they found the street there was crowded, and it seemed an activity was being held.

"The princess is going to throw a silk ball today. Whoever catches the ball will be the princess' husband," a person told them.

"Who is the girl in the temple then?" Monkey felt a little strange and decided to go together with his master to watch the ball game.

Upon noticing Monk Xuanzang amid the crowd, the princess threw the ball towards him intentionally. Then a group of people took Xuanzang into the royal palace.

"Now you are the princess' husband," the king said to Xuanzang.

"But …." Before Xuanzang could refuse, Monkey whispered to him, "Master, you stay here first and I will rescue you later."

Xuanzang had no other option but to agree.

On the occasion of the wedding ceremony, Xuanzang's disciples were invited into the royal palace again.

As soon as the princess walked out, Monkey noticed that she looked witchy. So he said to the fake princess, "Who are you, demon? How dare you pretend to be the princess?"

Because she knew she couldn't defeat Monkey King, the fake princess ran away immediately, whereupon Monkey started to chase after her.

When Monkey caught up with the demon intending to kill her, Fairy Chang'e arrived.

"She is my Jade Rabbit. Please don't kill her," Chang'e said to Monkey.

Then the Jade Rabbit was taken away by Chang'e. Monkey told the truth to the king and the real princess returned to the palace in the end.

37. Acquiring the Buddhist Scriptures

After experiencing numerous hardships, Monk Xuanzang and his disciples finally reached Western Heaven.

The Buddha said to his two disciples, "Ananda, Kasyapa, please take Xuanzang to get the Buddhist scriptures."

Afterwards, they arrived at the Sutra Storage Pavilion. Before Xuanzang and his disciples took the Buddhist scriptures, Ananda stopped them.

"Don't rush. Please show us your gifts first," Ananda said with a smile.

"We didn't expect the need for gifts!" Monk Xuanzang said.

"Without gifts, you cannot obtain the scriptures," Kasyapa followed.

"If you don't give us the scriptures, we will turn to the Buddha," Monkey replied furiously.

Ananda interrupted without delay, "Please don't do that! We will offer you the scriptures right now."

Having obtained the Buddhist scriptures, Monk Xuanzang and his disciples left with great delight.

As they went on their way, a large bird flew towards them and snatched the scriptures away. But when Monkey was about to give chase, the bird dropped them on the ground, so they all hurried to pick them up.

At that moment, Monk Xuanzang said with great surprise, "Why are there no words on the scriptures?"

In fact, what Ananda and Kasyapa had originally given them were fake scriptures.

They lost no time in turning to the Buddha for help.

The Buddha said with a smile, "I already know."

The Buddha asked his two disciples to take the travelers to fetch the scriptures again. This time, Ananda and Kasyapa again asked for gifts. Monk Xuanzang had no option but to give them the Golden Bowl. Only in this way could they acquire the Buddhist scriptures.

The Eight Guardian Warriors would be the escorts of Xuanzang and his disciples on their way back to the Tang Empire. They flew in the sky accompanied by the warriors.

One immortal told the Buddha, "Monk Xuanzang and his disciples have suffered a lot, encountering 80 hardships on their way to acquire the scriptures."

The Buddha replied, "They should have to cope with 81 tribulations, so they will face a final one." With these words, he dispatched another immortal to chase Xuanzang.

As they flew on and on, Xuanzang and his disciples suddenly fell on the ground with the Eight Guardian Warriors out of sight.

"Master, are you all right?" Monkey sprang to his feet and came to his master quickly.

"It's nothing serious. There is a big river ahead. How shall we cross it?" Monk Xuanzang became worried.

"I will carry you across the river." An old tortoise swam towards them and was ready to carry them. This river was the Tongtian River, and it was the same old tortoise who once took them across the river.

Each of them rode on the tortoise's back happily. When they reached the center of this river, the tortoise asked Xuanzang unexpectedly, "Did you ask the Buddha the question from me the last time you were here?"

Monk Xuanzang had forgotten to do it. He was speechless and became red in the face.

The old tortoise understood. He was enraged and threw them all into the river.

"We must save the Buddhist scriptures," Monk Xuanzang yelled.

They hurried to salvage the scriptures. Fortunately, they were retrieved. Afterwards, the group came to the riverbank, where they aired out the Buddhist scriptures in the sunshine. This was the 81st hardship they experienced.

After returning to the Tang Empire, Monk Xuanzang and his disciples submitted the Buddhist scriptures to Emperor Taizong (598-649). The emperor was overjoyed and invited Xuanzang to teach him the scriptures.

At this moment, the Eight Warrior Guardians emerged. They took Xuanzang and his three disciples to Western Heaven, where the Buddha turned them into four immortals and restored the White Dragon Horse into a dragon.

Monkey whispered to Xuanzang, "Master, can you remove the gold ring on my head?"

Monk Xuanzang said with a smile, "Just touch your head."

As he touched it, Monkey found no ring on his head! He could not have felt happier. They began to listen to the Buddhist scriptures taught by the Buddha.

This is the story of how Xuanzang obtained the Buddhist scriptures from Western Heaven.

拔	*v.*	bá	pull out
白骨	*n.*	báigǔ	white bone (of the dead)
办	*v.*	bàn	host, hold
帮	*v.*	bāng	help
绑	*v.*	bǎng	tie up
报仇	*v.*	bàochóu	revenge, avenge
报应	*n.*	bàoyìng	due punishment, retribution
贬	*v.*	biǎn	degrade, demote
冰	*n.*	bīng	ice
兵器	*n.*	bīngqì	weapon
并	*conj.*	bìng	and
藏	*v.*	cáng	hide
铲除	*v.*	chǎnchú	eradicate, eliminate
长生不老	*v.*	chángshēng-bùlǎo	live forever and never grow old, be immortal
嘲笑	*v.*	cháoxiào	deride, ridicule
沉	*adj.*	chén	heavy
盛	*v.*	chéng	ladle out
臭虫	*n.*	chòuchong	bedbug
穿山甲	*n.*	chuānshānjiǎ	pangolin
传	*v.*	chuán	pass on (knowledge, skill, etc.)
床	*n.*	chuáng	bed
催眠	*v.*	cuīmián	lull sb. to sleep, hypnotize
打赌	*v.*	dǎdǔ	bet
大战	*v.*	dà zhàn	fight a fierce battle
当年	*n.*	dāngnián	at that time, then
祷告	*v.*	dǎogào	pray for
道观	*n.*	dàoguàn	Taoist temple
道士	*n.*	dàoshi	Taoist priest
第	*aux.*	dì	(used before a numeral to form an ordinal number)
叼	*v.*	diāo	hold in the mouth

吊	*v.*	diào	hang, suspend
盯	*v.*	dīng	stare at
懂事	*v.*	dǒngshì	be sensible or considerate
动	*v.*	dòng	move
端	*v.*	duān	carry, hold something level with both hands
而已	*interj.*	éryǐ	that's all, nothing more, just
法术	*n.*	fǎshù	magic power
犯	*v.*	fàn	commit (a crime), make (a mistake)
饭菜	*n.*	fàncài	meal, food
房子	*n.*	fángzi	house
飞	*v.*	fēi	fly
愤怒	*adj.*	fènnù	angry, wrathful
风	*n.*	fēng	wind
佛经	*n.*	fójīng	Buddhist scriptures
符	*n.*	fú	talisman, magical figures drawn to invoke or expel spirits and bring good or ill fortune
斧子	*n.*	fǔzi	axe
改	*v.*	gǎi	correct, change
肝	*n.*	gān	liver
告状	*v.*	gàozhuàng	lodge a complaint against someone
各种各样	*adj.*	gè zhǒng gè yàng	various, all kinds of
工匠	*n.*	gōngjiàng	craftsman
公鸡	*n.*	gōngjǐ	rooster
宫殿	*n.*	gōngdiàn	palace
咕	*onom.*	gū	(of a hen) cluck
刮	*v.*	guā	(wind) blow
怪	*v.*	guài	blame
管	*v.*	guǎn	manage, take care of
柜子	*n.*	guìzi	cabinet, cupboard
跪	*v.*	guì	kneel, go down on one's knees
棍子	*n.*	gùnzi	stick
国丈	*n.*	guózhàng	king's father-in-law
海	*n.*	hǎi	ocean, sea
害	*v.*	hài	harm

旱灾	*n.*	hànzāi	drought
和尚	*n.*	héshang	monk
轰	*onom.*	hōng	bang, boom
猴王	*n.*	hóuwáng	monkey king
后	*n.*	hòu	afterwards
狐狸	*n.*	húli	fox
黄毛鼠	*n.*	huángmáoshǔ	yellow marten
活	*v.*	huó	live (up)
活儿	*n.*	huór	chores, work, job
伙	*m.w.*	huǒ	group, crowd
记	*v.*	jì	remember, memorize
记住	*v.*	jìzhù	remember, bear in mind
袈裟	*n.*	jiāshā	a patchwork outer vestment worn by a Buddhist monk
尖	*adj.*	jiān	pointed
间	*m.w.*	jiān	(used for rooms)
剪	*v.*	jiǎn	cut, trim
见	*v.*	jiàn	see
剑	*n.*	jiàn	sword
街	*n.*	jiē	street
结拜	*v.*	jiébài	become sworn brothers or sisters
戒尺	*n.*	jièchǐ	(in ancient China) teacher's paddle used for punishing pupils
斤	*m.w.*	jīn	*jin*, a unit for measuring weight equaling 0.5 kilograms
金	*adj.*	jīn	golden
金箍	*n.*	jīngū	gold ring, gold hoop
金鱼	*n.*	jīnyú	goldfish
紧	*adj.*	jǐn	tight
尽头	*n.*	jìntóu	end
惊	*v.*	jīng	be shocked, be stunned
竟敢	*v.*	jìng gǎn	dare, have the audacity
救命	*v.*	jiùmìng	help, save one's life
砍头	*v.*	kǎn tóu	chop off the head
客气	*adj.*	kèqi	polite, courteous
恳求	*v.*	kěnqiú	beg sincerely, implore

啦	*part.*	la	(used at the end of a sentence to indicate exclamation)
篮子	*n.*	lánzi	basket
捞	*v.*	lāo	scoop up from a liquid, dredge up
老妇人	*n.*	lǎofùrén	old lady
老公公	*n.*	lǎogōnggong	old man, grandpa
里面	*n.*	lǐmiàn	inside
炼丹	*v.*	liàndān	make pills (as a Taoist practice)
凉	*adj.*	liáng	cool, cold
裂	*v.*	liè	crack, break open, split
另	*pron.*	lìng	another, other
流	*v.*	liú	flow
露	*v.*	lù	expose
鹿	*n.*	lù	deer
旅馆	*n.*	lǚguǎn	hotel, inn
落	*v.*	luò	fall
嘛	*part.*	ma	(used to indicate that sth. is obvious)
埋怨	*v.*	mányuàn	blame, complain
们	*suf.*	men	(added after a personal pronoun or a noun to show plural number)
迷迷糊糊		mímíhūhū	in a daze
面前	*n.*	miànqián	presence
名声	*n.*	míngshēng	reputation
那么	*adv.*	nàme	so
难	*n.*	nàn	suffering, tribulation
闹	*v.*	nào	stir up trouble, cause chaos
尿	*n.*	niào	urine
女王	*n.*	nǚwáng	queen
女婿	*n.*	nǚxu	son-in-law
牌位	*n.*	páiwèi	memorial tablet
跑	*v.*	pǎo	run
琵琶	*n.*	pípa	*pipa*, a Chinese stringed musical instrument with a fretted fingerboard that was historically plucked with a pick, but is now mainly plucked with the fingers
偏偏	*adv.*	piānpiān	willfully, insistently
骗子	*n.*	piànzi	swindler, cheater

扑	*v.*	pū	pounce on, attack
扑灭	*v.*	pūmiè	put out (fire)
瀑布	*n.*	pùbù	waterfall
欺负	*v.*	qīfu	bully
奇遇	*n.*	qíyù	adventure
气 [1]	*v.*	qì	become angry
气 [2]	*n.*	qì	air, breath
强盗	*n.*	qiángdào	bandit
请帖	*n.*	qǐngtiě	invitation card
求	*v.*	qiú	beg
求雨	*v.*	qiú yǔ	pray for rain
惹祸	*v.*	rěhuò	make trouble
认错	*v.*	rèncuò	admit a mistake, make an apology
肉	*n.*	ròu	meat, flesh
撒尿	*v.*	sāniào	urinate
三更	*n.*	sāngēng	midnight
嫂子	*n.*	sǎozi	sister-in-law
山	*n.*	shān	mountain, hill
山洞	*n.*	shāndòng	cave
扇	*v.*	shān	wave, fan
伤	*v.*	shāng	hurt
烧	*v.*	shāo	burn
神奇	*adj.*	shénqí	magical
神水	*n.*	shénshuǐ	holy water
神仙	*n.*	shénxiān	an immortal who has supernatural power
神像	*n.*	shénxiàng	god statue
声	*n.*	shēng	sound
师弟	*n.*	shīdì	junior male apprentice
师父	*n.*	shīfu	master, an honorific title especially used by apprentices or disciples to address those who teach them craftsmanship
师妹	*n.*	shīmèi	junior sister apprentice
师徒	*n.*	shītú	master and disciple
石猴	*n.*	shíhóu	stone monkey
收服	*v.*	shōufú	bring under control
收集	*v.*	shōují	collect, gather

293

手	*n.*	shǒu	hand
手掌	*n.*	shǒuzhǎng	palm
受	*v.*	shòu	suffer from, be subjected to
熟	*adj.*	shú	cooked, done (food)
树林	*n.*	shùlín	woods, forest
摔	*v.*	shuāi	throw, fling
水沟	*n.*	shuǐgōu	ditch
睡着	*v.*	shuìzháo	fall asleep
丝	*n.*	sī	silk
寺庙	*n.*	sìmiào	temple
塔	*n.*	tǎ	tower, pagoda
弹	*v.*	tán	play (musical instrument like piano, guitar, etc.)
掏	*v.*	tāo	draw out, pull out
桃核	*n.*	táohé	peach stone, peach pit
特意	*adv.*	tèyì	on purpose, specially
踢	*v.*	tī	kick
替	*v.*	tì	replace
天	*n.*	tiān	day
跳	*v.*	tiào	jump, leap
调戏	*v.*	tiáoxì	flirt with
贴	*v.*	tiē	stick to, paste
听话	*v.*	tīnghuà	be obedient
偷吃	*v.*	tōu chī	take food sneakily
头 [1]	*n.*	tóu	head
头 [2]	*m.w.*	tóu	(used for animals like pigs, cows, etc.)
徒弟	*n.*	túdì	apprentice, disciple
土	*n.*	tǔ	soil, earth
外甥	*n.*	wàisheng	nephew
王宫	*n.*	wánggōng	imperial palace
王后	*n.*	wánghòu	queen, king's wife
网	*n.*	wǎng	net
乌龟	*n.*	wūguī	tortoise
蜈蚣	*n.*	wúgōng	centipede
误	*v.*	wù	mistake

锡杖	*n.*	xīzhàng	monk's cane with a tin ring or rings at the head
戏弄	*v.*	xìnòng	make fun of, play tricks on
仙丹	*n.*	xiāndān	elixir
仙女	*n.*	xiānnǚ	fairy maiden
箱子	*n.*	xiāngzi	box, trunk
小河	*n.*	xiǎo hé	stream, small river
蝎子	*n.*	xiēzi	scorpion
信	*n.*	xìn	letter
修炼	*v.*	xiūliàn	practice asceticism
绣球	*n.*	xiùqiú	ball of colorful silk strips
虚名	*n.*	xūmíng	title carrying no privilege, undeserved name
许	*v.*	xǔ	allow, permit (usually used as negative form)
炫耀	*v.*	xuànyào	show off, flaunt
压	*v.*	yā	press, weigh down
羊	*n.*	yáng	goat
养	*v.*	yǎng	raise, keep, grow
以后	*n.*	yǐhòu	afterwards
以免	*conj.*	yǐmiǎn	lest
引	*v.*	yǐn	lure, attract
鹰	*n.*	yīng	eagle
用力	*v.*	yònglì	exert oneself physically
油	*n.*	yóu	oil
游	*v.*	yóu	swim
有点儿	*adv.*	yǒu diǎnr	a little, a bit
遇	*v.*	yù	encounter, meet
远处	*n.*	yuǎnchù	distant place
院子	*n.*	yuànzi	yard
砸	*v.*	zá	pound, smash
贼	*n.*	zéi	thief
扎	*v.*	zhā	prick, jab
炸	*v.*	zhá	fry
占卜	*v.*	zhānbǔ	practice divination
战袍	*n.*	zhànpáo	war robe

张扬	*v.*	zhāngyáng	show off, make known
遮	*v.*	zhē	cover, hide from view
这么	*adv.*	zhème	so, such
这样	*pron.*	zhèyàng	such, like this
针	*n.*	zhēn	needle
珍贵	*adj.*	zhēnguì	precious, valuable
只不过	*adv.*	zhǐbuguò	only, just
智斗	*v.*	zhìdòu	fight with wisdom
钟	*n.*	zhōng	clock, bell
咒语	*n.*	zhòuyǔ	incantation, spell
柱子	*n.*	zhùzi	pillar
爪子	*n.*	zhuǎzi	claw, paw
壮	*adj.*	zhuàng	strong
钻	*v.*	zuān	get into, go through
昨晚	*n.*	zuówǎn	last night
坐禅	*v.*	zuòchán	sit in meditation
坐骑	*n.*	zuòjì	beast for riding

项目策划：刘小琳　韩　颖
责任编辑：刘小琳
英文编辑：吴爱俊
英文审定：黄长奇　James Hutchison
插图绘制：硕果儿
设计指导：isles studio
设计制作：isles studio

图书在版编目（CIP）数据

西游记 ／（明）吴承恩原著；李梓萌，马娴改编．—
北京：华语教学出版社，2017
（"彩虹桥"汉语分级读物．6级：2500词）
ISBN 978-7-5138-1329-7

Ⅰ．①西… Ⅱ．①吴… ②李… ③马… Ⅲ．①汉语－
对外汉语教学－语言读物 Ⅳ．① H195.5

中国版本图书馆 CIP 数据核字（2017）第 015062 号

西游记

[明] 吴承恩　原著

李梓萌　马　娴　改编

潘婉雯　李佳星　李君婷　丁　力　靳航航　陈碧兰　翻译

*

© 华语教学出版社有限责任公司
华语教学出版社有限责任公司出版
（中国北京百万庄大街 24 号 邮政编码 100037）
电话：(86)10-68320585, 68997826
传真：(86)10-68997826, 68326333
网址：www.sinolingua.com.cn
电子信箱：hyjx@sinolingua.com.cn
北京京华虎彩印刷有限公司印刷
2017 年（32 开）第 1 版
2019 年第 1 版第 2 次印刷
（汉英）
ISBN 978-7-5138-1329-7
定价：49.00 元